The *Best* of

Spiritual Writers Network

2016

PRESENTED BY

SPIRITUAL WRITERS NETWORK

&

TRANSCENDENT PUBLISHING

Transcendent
——Publishing——

Spiritual Writers Network
Presents

The Best of Spiritual Writers Network 2016

Transcendent Publishing
PO Box 66202
St. Pete Beach, FL 33736
www.TranscendentPublishing.com

ISBN-10: 0-9982869-7-4
ISBN-13: 978-0-9982869-7-6

Compiled by Shanda Trofe

Printed in the United States of America

This book is dedicated to the writers, poets, and artists of the world. The ones committed to touching our hearts and lifting our spirits—one word, one poem, and one story at a time.

CONTENTS

"Every secret of a writer's soul, every experience of his life, every quality of his mind, is written large in his works."
—Virginia Woolf

THE HANDS OF LOVE

By Louise Huey Greenleaf

1st Place Winner

It is a song my daughter, Krissy, and I used to sing along with the character, *The Count*, on the children's television show, *Sesame Street,* called *HANDS,* written by *Jeff Moss*. It was during her toddler years when we watched the show every weekday morning. The program was such a great aid in helping the youngest of children to learn about common and valuable life lessons on nature, math, science, the environment, how our bodies work, as well as animals—just about *anything*.

We so enjoyed watching it together and participating in the wonderful songs, knowing and loving *all* the characters including the humans—as if they were part of our own family. It was way back then, in the beginning years with multiple sclerosis, that I realized the importance of the functions in our bodies. Not only because I was so amazed by my own one-and-a-half-year-old's rapid development and ability to learn quickly, and with such joy and enthusiasm, but also, even back then, because the sensations in my hands I was feeling were oddly unusual. Yes, even back then, my hands were functioning normally for the most part, but beginning to show noticeable signs that their abilities were not as sharp as I had always known them to be for all of my 25 years. I was left with having no choice other than to fight my way through the disturbing changes in order to maintain the functions that are essential to carry on with the countless tasks of not only life in general, but more importantly, to take care of myself, and fulfill my responsibilities as a wife and mother. Certainly, there is *no* human being or living creature that deserves to experience this—let alone endure such excruciating pain and the severe lessening capabilities that our very lives depend on. My baby needed me, and I wasn't going to give into the cruel monster that had invaded not only my body, but our lives, as mother and daughter, and our life as a family with daddy too. She was an innocent, happy little girl who had no clue as to what was stirring inside of me, her mommy who loved her beyond words.

I daresay it was my hands, especially, I had to constantly keep focus on so that I could raise her properly by doing what moms and wives do for our families, ourselves, and others in need. So it was through this song that I realized from the first time I heard it, how our hands surely are the *most* important tools we have. The wonderful thing is that God gave us two, one attached to each of our arms, which are equipped with all the nerves, muscles, and tendons that allow our hands to properly serve us, performing tasks such as opening and closing, reaching and grabbing, pushing and pulling, grasping and carrying, lifting and holding. Yes, I know firsthand one can live a very functional life without the use of their legs. I have done that for over 37 years now! However, our hands and arms are, without doubt, our *most* essential and useful parts. Sadly, I have lost almost full function in my right hand, but my left, thankfully, is my dominant and working well, although in all certainty it has its issues.

As I sit here speaking into my computer screen because of the limited use in both hands, due to the consequential inflictions of living life with a progressive and incurable disease, I am grateful for the high-level technology has come to us to provide ways to achieve despite disability, such as this voice dictation program allowing me to write this story. Would I rather be typing the words? The answer is yes, and even further still, would I rather be holding a pen in my hand and writing on paper in order to carry out the task? The answer is, you bet, more than I pray you or anyone you love will ever know.

So here are the words to the song, *HANDS*, written by *Jeff Moss,* sung by the notoriously non-cynical, distinctly loved, highly mysterious, yet delightfully friendly, optimistic, and trusting vampire Muppet character on *Sesame Street—The Count.*

A mouth can talk, a mouth can chew,
not many things a mouth can do.
But hands, just mention hands and my heart sings!
For hands can do so many, many things.

Your hands can brush your teeth or comb your hair,
throw a ball into the air,
wave hello, or wave goodbye,
even make a pizza pie;
use a fork or use a spoon,
hold a string on a balloon,
paint a picture, tie your shoe,
so many things your hands can do.

A nose can breathe, a nose can smell,
not many things a nose does well.
But hands can do so many things for you.
I've mentioned some, now let me add a few.

Your hands can turn the pages of a book,
pick a phone up off the hook,
rub your nose, scratch your head,
flip a coin, or make your bed,
push a button, write your name,
pat a dog or play a game,
pick a flower, yes it's true,
so very many things your hands can do.

Your hands can strum a guitar, or they can dig in the sand, or they can clap for someone, or they can turn on the faucet, or they can shake hands with other hands, they can ring door bells, button buttons, zip zippers, tie a knot—climb a tree!

I can reflect back on my life from when I was a little girl picking up and holding my dollies, brushing their hair and dressing them. Brushing my own hair and dressing my own self, swinging a jump rope, and swimming! Eating an ice cream cone and rubbing my mom's back.

When I grew into a teen, I learned to play instruments to make beautiful music, such as the piano, guitar, and fife. I led the Drum Corps with a long baton in parades. I learned to drive a car, and threw my graduation cap up into the air to celebrate the end of all that was familiar and safe, and retrieved it in my hands when it fell back down. Then my hands turned into wings as I flew off to learn about life and the ways to grow in wisdom.

When I became a woman and met my lifelong partner, my hands placed a ring to represent my promised, forever love on his finger, and he placed one on mine. Then together as one, our four hands built a cozy nest where we planted a seed. When the seed came to bloom, she was my mini me, then all of our hands as a whole equaled six between us three.

I joyfully used my hands to pick my baby up and cradle her in my arms. They caressed her silky soft skin, and guided my breasts to her mouth to nourish her body so she would grow strong and healthy. They changed her diapers to keep her dry and comfortable. They wiped her little tears when she was unhappy, and carefully clipped her little nails so they wouldn't scratch her. They covered my eyes when we played peek-a-boo and opened wide and away when I said, "I see you!"

When she began to walk, my hands lifted her when she fell. They pushed her on the swing at the park. "Higher, mommy, push me higher!" she would joyfully shout. They lifted her onto the horsey at the mall, and slipped a quarter into the slot so she could go 'round and 'round. They handed her a free cookie from the bakery lady at the grocery store each week—YUM!

I am blessed and grateful beyond measure to say that even though my hands no longer have the ability to do the tasks they could from the day my daughter was born until she grew up and began her own journey, still I am fulfilled knowing that I DID take care of my family with MY OWN able hands with GREAT love and joy!

I am now 57 years old, and have battled MS for my entire adult life. But no matter my losses, or how I will continue to progress, I reign victorious knowing I have fulfilled my life's purpose. With the help of Jesus, I have done my job as a loving wife, mother, and blessed and faithful child of God, and I will continue to exercise my lifelong dream as a writer, poet, and author, knowing that self love and happiness is rewarded when we consciously make the choice to move forward, regardless of the hardships we face. In this we have found the true definition of what it is to be courageous, even if it is just by taking baby steps, pushing the wheels forward in my case, despite the inability to do what *most* need not give thought to doing, how many times in the course of a day. For instance, standing up from a sitting position, or vice versa, going up and down steps, getting on and off the toilet, grabbing something out of the refrigerator to eat, washing dishes, getting the mail, getting in and out of the car, doing a load of laundry to dry, to fold, to put away. Grabbing an item that's hanging in a closet or hanging something up, reaching for an item in an overhead cabinet, putting your legs and feet up to relax, and doing these things ALL BY YOURSELF without help from anyone, because it is simply what *most* are able to do, automatically and spontaneously.

For people like me who are physically disadvantaged and wheelchair-bound, these tasks can be challenging and frustrating, to say the least, when trying to simply live our lives as normally as possible, while at the same time, dealing with the constant difficulties that come up throughout the day—let alone for the duration of a lifetime! Through the years, many people have said to me, "I couldn't do it!" Well I'm here to tell you, YES YOU CAN! I have, and don't like it, wouldn't wish living this way on the worst offender on earth. But, when faced with no other choice, you find a way. Then you make the decision to continue to move forward, if you want to live the best life you can.

As you grow in acceptance, you embrace your faith in God, become stronger, and you persevere. You learn everything that's REALLY cruddy, and what's MOST wonderful, about yourself. You learn to ride the rises and plunges of the waves, and you learn to accept yourself for WHO YOU ARE, because what you are physically has NOTHING to do with who you are in your soul—the part of you who is eternal, the part of you NOTHING can change. The part that was ALWAYS meant to be. I have finally accepted the fact that I AM ENOUGH, just the way I am!

Though there is still no cure for multiple sclerosis, the generous funds that are raised throughout the world have allowed the brilliant minds and dedicated, loving hands of researchers and scientists the ability to develop medications and apparatuses that have brought great relief to those who are afflicted with not only MS, but *many* other chronic diseases as well.

In this human fraternity, let us join our loving hands together in thought, prayer, and with compassionate hearts for ALL of the men, women and children who suffer with chronic diseases, whatever they may be.

Louise Huey Greenleaf is an award-winning author and poet who exercises her love of writing by sharing her heartfelt words of inspiration with the world, especially to those who live in adverse situations such as her own.

*Her works are included in five multi-authored books with Spiritual Writers Network/Transcendent Publishing. *Touched by an Angel: A Collection of Divinely Inspired Stories and Poems/Titanium Angel, *Whispers of the Soul: A Poetry Anthology—(3rd Place Quarterly Contest Winner)/SUCCUMP-TION-ACITY, *The Best of Spiritual Writers Network 2014/A Precious Memory, *Illuminations of the Soul: A Poetry Anthology/Millions of Reasons to Smile Today, *Finding Our Wings: An Angelic Collection of Stories and Poems (Title by Krista Gawronski and Louise Huey Greenleaf)/Angels Watching Over Me, *The Invisible Thread ~ Real Stories of Synchronicity with Sunny Dawn Johnston and Friends/Silky Tales of Eternal Grace, published by OptiMystic Press. Email: louisehgreenleaf@gmail.com; Facebook: www.facebook.com/louisehueygreenleaf*

LEAP OF FAITH

By Mary Frances Fisher

2ⁿᵈ *Place Winner*

There was no doubt about it. Heaven was overcrowded and a prompt solution was required to restore harmonious balance. Clouds were teeming with family members jockeying for space and disturbing the normal tranquility. God was not happy. With over a thousand souls arriving hourly, the problem was getting out of hand. God called forth Michelangelo—a master architect in addition to his infamous painting and sculpture extravaganzas. A plan was devised to expand Heaven by three million miles, separated by realms to please the eye and ease the tension.

Work was begun immediately and, despite the enormous nature of the task at hand, God breathed a sigh of relief. Word spread throughout Heaven and all were anxious to see the new and improved masterpiece, surely Michelangelo's best work to date. To prevent accidents, signs were posted around the construction borders warning all inhabitants of the dangers. With a strict penalty imposed should anyone disobey the directive, no one wanted to risk the threatened change in status that would result. After all, once you've seen Heaven, why would you risk losing it? Everyone stayed far away from the construction area except one . . .

† † †

Agnes led a lonely existence for as long as she could recall. Petite and short in stature, her voice was but a whisper easily ignored by others. She was orphaned at a young age when her parents died in an auto accident after their Model T lost control and wrapped itself around a tree. Sixteen year old Agnes was asleep in the back seat and emerged unscathed.

Plain in appearance wearing hand-me-down clothes and unkempt long brown hair, she was never adopted and kept to herself. Agnes felt like a ghost—invisible to all around her and inconsequential in the grand scheme of things. Despite her kind nature and willingness to assist others, favors were never reciprocated and deemed insignificant—after all, it was *just* Agnes.

Released from the orphanage at age eighteen with twenty-five dollars cash and a bus ticket to any city in England, she chose Edinburgh. Agnes had always been drawn to the sea, mainly from picture books and descriptions on radio broadcasts, and she looked forward to a life of adventure. This would be her first major disappointment. She drifted through her new life by the sea as invisible as ever. Agnes drew into herself and created her own circle of imaginary friends through books and collected a variety of pets. Resigned to be a spinster, Agnes worked in a library and returned directly home each night where she fixed a can of soup, two pieces of toast, and curled up on the couch with a good book and her calico cat asleep in her lap. Life wasn't perfect, but Agnes was happy.

Two years after Agnes moved to Edinburgh, she began to experience abdominal pains. She visited the local pharmacy and was given a bottle of Paregoric to ease the discomfort. When her symptoms intensified, Agnes reported to a local clinic. Several tests were run and she was advised to return in two weeks for the results. Despite her anxiety and fear of the unknown, Agnes told no one and suffered in silence.

Reporting to her doctor exactly two weeks later, Agnes was informed, quite bluntly, that she had inoperable cancer. With only two months to live, she was advised to get her affairs in order. Agnes reeled from the startling news, and the callous manner in which it was delivered, but remained stoic as she walked unsteadily into her tiny apartment. Thanks to her frugal nature, Agnes had saved a tidy sum of money and decided to live before she died.

Agnes reported to work at eight o'clock the next morning, punctual as always, and gave her notice. Loath to incur sympathy, she provided no excuse and walked out with her head held high as her heart pounded wildly. On her way back home, Agnes passed a travel agency with promises of enticing adventures for a meager price. With her newfound confidence, she booked several tours over a two month period. Her first excursion involved major countries in Europe with a final destination of America. After spending a week in America to see firsthand the highlights she read about in her books, Agnes would tour the Orient. Life was grand!

She returned home and started to pack. Agnes went to the nearest passport office and received her first official document proudly displaying her name. Agnes had finally arrived! The remainder of the week was filled with assorted tasks—canceling her apartment, arranging for transport to the shipyard, finding homes for her pets, and giving away personal possessions to charity. No longer willing to wear sensible shoes and drab clothes, she went on a shopping spree that delighted and terrified her.

When Agnes arrived at the dock and glimpsed the magnificent ship that would transport her to another country, she was ecstatic. Wearing a completely new outfit, including the latest hat with a colorful feather, she drew the stares of many men as she boarded the vessel. Her remaining time on earth would be perfect.

On the first night of the cruise, Agnes ventured from her cabin wearing one of her favorite outfits—a long paisley gown with a scooped neck and lace-capped three-quarter length sleeves complimented by a new hat, dainty button-up shoes, and a parasol. It happened again! Men actually stared as she walked by and Agnes was thrilled to be noticed. One man in particular, approached her cautiously.

"Excuse me, Miss. I don't mean to bother you, but I couldn't help but admire your lovely outfit. Would you join me for dinner tonight?"

Once Agnes found her voice, she quietly replied with a poise that astonished her, "It would be my delight. My name is Agnes and yours ..."

"Forgive me. Your beauty clouded my manners. My name is Hiram Goldberg."

"It's a pleasure to meet you, Hiram."

"The pleasure is all mine. Shall I pick you up at seven o'clock?"

Clearly a man of means, Agnes was concerned that he would see her lower class accommodations. "Why don't we meet at the top of the staircase at 7:00? That way we can make a grand entrance." Agnes couldn't believe she spoke those words but, with nothing left to lose, a little boldness would surely be forgiven.

When a sudden wind picked up and threatened to blow Agnes's hat overboard, she retired to her room. The excitement had been overwhelming. That afternoon, for the first time in her life, she visited the beauty parlor and her long auburn locks were entwined around her head and adorned with sparkling clips. Selecting another favorite outfit, one more appropriate for an evening affair—emerald green silk gown, ivory shawl, and patent-leather shoes with two inch heels—she made her way to the main dining hall.

True to his word, Hiram met her at the top of the staircase at precisely seven o'clock. At first glance, he took her breath away in his perfectly attired tuxedo, dark wavy hair combed back, and holding a single red rose in his hand.

When he caught sight of Agnes, Hiram bowed and presented her with the rose. "A beautiful flower for a beautiful lady." Agnes blushed and couldn't believe her good fortune. Dinner was wonderful, the champagne chilled to perfection, and desserts guaranteed to pop her corset.

Each afternoon, they sat in deck chairs reading and talking about their hopes and dreams. Agnes didn't mention her dreams would be short-lived. Every night they met at the top of the staircase and drew stares from men and woman alike as they descended to dine on a meal fit for royalty.

After dinner on the fourth night, they walked along the upper deck and a sudden chill hit the air. Hiram gave Agnes his coat when she began to shiver.

"Perhaps we should go downstairs for a nightcap. Something to warm you up."

"I'd like that."

Arm in arm they descended to the lounge and Hiram brought two brandy snifters to a corner table. After drinking half his brandy Hiram stated, "I hope you don't mind, but I have a brief business appointment. Please wait for me. I shan't be long."

"Of course. I will count the minutes until you return." Hiram bent down and kissed Agnes's hand. She was truly the luckiest woman in the world!

Slowly sipping her brandy, Agnes felt a warm tingling throughout her body—an altogether pleasant sensation. But, when thirty minutes passed and Hiram didn't return, Agnes convinced herself that she was a fool. She rose from her chair, intent on returning to her room before any more embarrassment.

"Don't tell me that you're leaving already. I still have to finish my brandy."

Agnes blushed at her momentary lapse of confidence and replied, "I didn't want you to feel any pressure about cutting your meeting short."

"Nonsense. I'd much rather spend time with you than attending to business." Hiram's tone became somber as he asked a most unusual question. "I have a favor to ask—one that may sound strange but it is very important that you listen to my advice. Will you do that for me?"

At first Agnes wasn't sure what to think. Was their time together a ruse? Did Hiram have an ulterior motive? Agnes tentatively replied, "I shall try. First tell me what you need me to do."

Hiram succinctly told Agnes what was required and she reluctantly agreed. Following his instructions to the letter, Hiram embraced Agnes and promised he would see her soon. Agnes found herself looking forlornly at the water as waves lapped around the boat. She began to experience pain in her abdomen and thought, *Not now!*

Ignoring her own pain while sitting in the small boat, crowded with frightened women and children, Agnes became the voice of reason and her calm demeanor comforted others. With frightening speed, the *Titanic* sunk as screams from the less fortunate echoed in the dark, cold night. Help would arrive too late for most as remaining passengers cowered together in a collective despair as they were plunged into an ice-cold watery grave.

Out of the corner of her eye, Agnes noticed a young boy had fallen overboard from another lifeboat close by—one that was overfilled with passengers anxious to save only themselves and ignorant of the boy's plight. Without regard for her safety, Agnes took off her lifejacket and leaned over as far as possible to extend the lifeline. The boy grabbed onto it with a force that startled Agnes and propelled her out of the boat into the icy water. Unable to swim, Agnes could feel the sea pull her into its icy grasp but not before she saw the young lad pulled onto her boat. As she continued to sink, Agnes thought wistfully, *I've always been drawn to the sea but never dreamed it would be my final resting place.*

When she opened her eyes, Agnes was confused and frightened. The room was startlingly white filled with exotic flowers and the most beautiful music she'd ever heard. She looked in a reflecting pool and was surprised to see her outfit dry and completely undamaged—even her hair was perfectly coiffed! Venturing out of the room in search of answers, Agnes was greeted kindly with offers to help and reassurances that she wasn't dreaming.

Trying to get her bearings, Agnes felt like she was walking on air and practically ran into Hiram's arms.

"You see, my darling, I told you that it wouldn't be long before we would meet again."

"Oh, Hiram, is it really you?"

Hugging her closely and giving her a passionate kiss, Hiram softly replied, "Of course, my love." Still reeling from the depth of Hiram's kiss, Agnes followed Hiram as he gave her the grand tour. Time stood still and they spent every moment together, falling in love and reveling in their newfound passion.

At the appointed time, Hiram took Agnes into his arms and said, "Remember what I told you before I placed you in the lifeboat?"

"You said we would be together shortly."

"That's right. Now I need you to have faith in me once again when I tell you that we shall be together shortly."

"But, Hiram, I don't understand. We *are* together. Why would you say …" Agnes's last sentence was interrupted as she fell into the gaping hole just one short step ahead of Hiram. She screamed during a fall that lasted a lifetime as past events replayed before her eyes in a dizzying array of colorful lights illuminating her path.

When Agnes awoke, she was in a beautiful mansion, complete with servants, riding stables, tennis courts, and enough food and delicacies to last a generation. Gingerly getting out of the soft featherbed, Agnes donned a robe and carefully ventured downstairs, her gait slightly unstable. On a mantle in the parlor was a picture of her beloved Hiram.

Approaching a servant, she inquired, "Where is Hiram?"

The maid gave her a frightened look, dropped a tray of food, and cautiously replied, "He died aboard the *Titanic.*"

Agnes felt faint and the maid led her to a chair. She placed Agnes's feet on a stool and brought her a snifter of brandy. Staring at this delicate reminder, Agnes began to cry. A doctor was sent for and, after a thorough exam, diagnosed Agnes with complete exhaustion.

Looking at Agnes as though she had risen from the dead, he quietly asked, "What's the last thing you remember?"

"Hiram placed me on a lifeboat and, after I gave my lifejacket to a boy who fell overboard, I, too, fell into the water. I was unable to swim and when I awoke, I found myself in a white room. When I tried to explore my surroundings—quite beautiful as I recall—I ran into Hiram and we spent the most delightful days together … Until I fell through a hole and woke up in this house."

Taken aback, the doctor replied softly, "Then it was you who saved my life."

Agnes stared in shock at the forty year old doctor. *It's not possible.*

"My dear," the doctor asked, "do you know what year it is?"

"Of course I do. It's 1912."

"No ... it's 1942. You've been in a coma for thirty years."

"That's not possible. I just saw Hiram moments ago."

Selecting his words carefully, the doctor explained. "Hiram was one of the engineers on board the *Titanic's* maiden voyage. While he was with you on the upper deck on that fateful night, he noticed the ice caps and estimated their depths would surely tear apart the ship's underbelly. Before the danger became acute, he cabled his attorney to make certain you were taken care of and lived your remaining years in his home. Or should I say, *your* home. After you rescued me, a sailor from the lifeboat dove into the freezing water and saved your life. You were transferred to a local hospital until Mr. Goldberg's solicitor tracked you down and brought you here."

"But I was only given two months to live ..."

"Who told you that?"

"A doctor shortly before I boarded the *Titanic*."

"He was mistaken. Other than being comatose, you've remained in perfect health and nurses round the clock have provided physical therapy to keep your muscles supple with full range of motion."

"This is all quite unbelievable."

"I understand, but Hiram must have loved you very much. I'm sorry he didn't survive to be here today."

"Oh but he is. He remains alive in my heart. Each night I can feel his arms envelope me in a tender embrace as he kisses my tears away."

"What a lovely thought, Agnes. I recommend you take things slowly and enjoy the wonderful life you've been given."

"I certainly intend to. Thank you, doctor."

After the doctor left, Agnes slowly walked through the rooms of her new home. She found a picture of Hiram as a boy standing next to a woman who closely resembled Agnes. *Why, we could have been twins! No wonder Hiram was drawn to me.*

Overwhelmed, Agnes sat in the nearest chair and closed her eyes. Hiram greeted her as she joined him in her dreams and they danced the night away. She would make the most of her time on earth until she would once again be reunited with Hiram. Agnes realized a giant leap of faith to attain true happiness was not required—merely the courage to take a small step into the unknown.

✝ ✝ ✝

Heaven was bustling with activity now that the renovations were complete. But the moment Agnes woke up, everyone stopped to celebrate the woman whose selfless act gave her a new lease on life after falling through a heavenly opening. Hiram was surrounded by family and friends as they gazed down with pride knowing Agnes's secret desires were finally realized. She was given a storybook life filled with friends, adventures, and endless possibilities. Life truly was grand!

THE END

Mary Frances Fisher, *a lifelong resident of Cleveland OH, has spent the majority of her career as a legal nurse consultant and signed with Taxi Modeling and Talent Agency as a commercial print model in 2012. With Germaine Moody and writer contributions from over 100 countries, she co-authored her first published work in 2013, 50 Seeds of Greatness (www.50seedsofgreatness.com). Her additional writing experiences include several short stories published by Transcendent Publishing: "Earning My Wings" in Touched by an Angel: A Collection of Divinely Inspired Stories and Poems, October 2013; "Mercy's Legacy" in Best of Spiritual Writers Network 2013, December 2013; "Be Careful What You Wish For" in The Best of Spiritual Writers Network 2014, January 2015; and "The Gift" in Finding Our Wings: A Collection of Angelic Stories and Poems, March 2016. Her novel, Paradox Forged in Blood, was published on August 24, 2016 by Cambron Publishing Group, LLC and she is currently working on a companion novel, Growing Up O'Malley. In addition, she has written a screenplay based on "Mercy's Legacy." Mary Frances lives in a suburb of Cleveland with her family.*

CHORUS OF THE FEMININE

By Katrina Elkins

3rd Place Winner

The chorus of the Feminine is within all humanity.

I can hear it.

Listen closely.

The Feminine brings a message.

In this moment, I have awakened to a new plane of reality.

I am forever and completely changed in the endless space of the Feminine landscape.

The bones long gone, now the vast open land holds the damage of the war waged.

A new beginning awaits our tender babes longing for the brave honesty from our wombs.

My ovaries beat to the new heartbeat of our Mother, no longer only a lullaby.

It is a quick awakening.

Only yesterday, I fed my newborn the nectar from my bosom over the grave of my grandmother.

The grief of loss, the grief of all that never was, is now a beacon, shining a floodlight on my truth.

Truths hidden deep within the land of my body.

The ache of the Feminine cannot be ignored.

Hiding is the opposite of the expansiveness of spirit called Holy.

Holy is within me.

The I AM is in my heart and shines through the miracle that is my existence.

The grief of the Feminine is my own grief buried in the recesses of my mind, and harbored in my heart. Long ago forgotten and already mourned, it shows me there is much work to do.

Now my flesh torn apart welcomes the continuous flood of immortal tears.

A new haven awaits within my body as I address this anguish of loss and grief.

The Feminine brings me to the deeper aches of humanity.

I am called to be a servant of love and a vessel of light, ready and willing to trust completely.

Oh, the grey dust longs to be cleared.

The ancient bones are gone and I am haunted by the uncertainty of this new place.

I AM haunted by all that it reveals as it implores me to surrender.

Complete surrender into the vessel of who I AM.

Complete surrender into the order of nature.

I rise up and I fall down. I fall down and I rise up.

I AM holds the power of igniting the fires within my dreams.

I AM supported by our Divine Mother and I AM ready.

Our Mother is part of the Feminine.

The devastation is real.

And the hunger is palpable.

My human body fragile with thoughts of suffering.

My spirit ready for all that is to be unraveled and loved again within me.

Today, the life force coursing through me is the fresh energy of the Feminine.

I have felt this energy, slowly expanding, into my human existence.

The bright, hot seduction of love.

I bow in honor of the beauty it generates within.

I have witnessed the glow of the Feminine. I honor the abundance of all that comes in stillness.

I am a woman.

I surrender to the Feminine.

I am a woman.

I open to the Feminine.

The sustenance of a river oozing with the golden nectar of the Divine.

The calling is now. The chorus.

The awakening is a ripple.

My hands clap on the mountaintops, in the swamps, and over the vastness of the ocean, creating the connection to all that will heal the hearts of humanity.

In my quietness, in the moment of complete surrender, I can hear it.

The croaking frogs at noon sing a song of the Feminine.

The timeless wisdom unfolds in my heart space and I AM at peace with this revealing. My ears yearn for the song I heard as a young child.

The sweetest chorus that ever graced my soul and tickled my toes. Its art heralds the vibration of Mother Earth.

My body quivers in the trust of letting go.

The voice, The Feminine. It is not an illusion born in the wild of nothingness.

The Feminine waits for the clearing of our lingering ghosts stuck in the passage of time.

I am a human.

I surrender to the Feminine.

I am human.

The quest to bring a new song.

An urge that transcends my everyday struggles.

I am open to receive the one energy that is the infinite Universe.

I once was frightened by my deepest emotions, so I turned them into dark ravines, canyons. Unwilling to explore the coursing of energy through my body.

Shutting down. Closing up and locking away my buried treasures, hoping no one would notice my resistance.

Now, I am on my knees, skin caked with the softness of the fertile valley within as my tears greet the new dawn of my longing.

I AM the Feminine energy.

The curtain is pulled back on the centuries of misplaced trust and raging anger.

The Feminine is begging me to walk with a lighter step.

Navigating the upheavals is part of the new vibration of love.

I AM a new song and I join the chorus.

It is time to be of service. The call is now.

I AM a new song ready to be sung.

I AM the universe within.

I welcome the Goddess of connection into my vibrant spiritual expansion.

Gazing in wonder at the silvery shadows of the moon that illuminate the path of my destiny gives me the courage to let go.

I surrender to the Feminine.

I AM the Chorus of the Feminine.

Unexpected and never forced.

I AM the new song that will lift up the youth from despair.

I AM the choir of the earth.

Sing with me in unison.

We are one. And we are Holy.

Katrina Elkins, author and a certified Breath of Love facilitator, is cultivating a new awareness of the power of self-love, community, and the true meaning of healing from old traumas. Having overcome a childhood lived in a fear-based, apocalyptic cult Katrina awakens us to the beauty of life in the present moment.

Katrina speaks of the ease and grace available to all, both men and women, from the Feminine. Her writings show fearlessness in following the soul's quest of discovering its true and boundless potential. She teaches that peace ignites from within and we are to greet it with love and compassion. Ultimately, we are meant to live connected and in alignment with the gifts and bounty of the Universe.

Her works are included in three multi-authored books. The Invisible Thread ~ Real Stories of Synchronicity with Sunny Dawn Johnston and Friends / Walk Through The Door, published by OptiMystic Press. The Peacemakers with Shanda Trofe and Louise Huey Greenleaf / Little Eagle, published by Transcendent Publishing and 365 Life Shifts~ Pivotal Moments That Changed Everything with Jodi Chapman / The Seer, published by DandiLove Unlimited.

Connect with Katrina

Email: Info@katrinaelkins.com

Website: www.katrinaelkins.com

Facebook: www.facebook.com/katrinaelkins

THE DREAM GIFT

By Maggie Honnold

The first time he saw it, he knew. Here was the perfect gift. Something she had wanted all of her life and never had, but now he would be the one to provide her heart's desire. Oh, she would be so surprised. First, that he could still gift her even now, and second, because the coloring and character was none of which she had ever been seen before in a living creature. The whiteness of the coat with only a few of the Appaloosa spots on the rump was outstanding. But it was the whiskers and the mane that drew him to this magnificent creature. Glowing in the sun of Heaven they looked translucent, giving off a soft, pink glow. He had yet to know how she would translate to the dream world below but He could not imagine that she would not be beautiful there also.

He caught up the sparkling reins and began to gently rub the velvety muzzle. The horse whinnied softly as she came under the spell of his touch. He always had a way with horses. His Midnight had been a beautiful horse but this gift, the white coat with the glowing pink whiskers, oh she would love it so. He knew she would not need a saddle. Just reigns and the flowing thick mane on which to grab should she feel herself sliding. He chuckled to himself of the stories she had told in the past about falling off her cousin's pony as a kid.

He made a clicking noise with his tongue and pulled gently on the reins in his hand, off they went…

It had been a restless night for her. She was constantly shifting positions and dreaming the oddest things that kept waking her. Looking at the clock once more, she rearranged herself around her faithful basset bed partner and dozed.

It was the world between wake and sleep when she first understood that he was with her. She felt a soft touch on her arm and as she turned she could smell his gift. She loved the scent of horses – every single part. She breathed deeply and looked at the white face before her. The pink whiskers stood out in the sun, glowing and beckoning for her touch. She reached for the soft muzzle and received a soft whiney and nudge for her effort. As she ran her fingers across the whiskers and nose, her right hand reached into the soft pink mane.

"Can I get on?" she asked the man standing at her side holding the reins.

He nodded, "she is a gift for you. Take her and ride, stable her with the other horses but ride her every day for she will wither without your attention and love."

She mounted and gripped the shoulders under her with her knees. She loved dreams – her knees didn't hurt. She chuckled to herself. Using her bare heels to communicate, "let's go" and felt the sure response of her wonderful gift as they began to trot down the dusty dirt road.

It wasn't long before they were galloping across fields, and over fallen logs. As a kid she would have fallen off with the jump but now all was different. Turning for home, she looked for him but he was gone.

Heading to the paddock area (she never had a paddock but this was a dream), she dismounted, removed the halter and turned her out into the field that was more green and vibrant than she had ever seen. Her new gift began to leisurely nibble.

Walking back to the house her mind turned to what it means to be loved for a lifetime, understanding that even now, her dreams can communicate longings that cannot be reached in her conscious mind.

Suddenly she knew it was over. The whine that wakened her was her basset, ThelmaLou, wanting to go outside. Morning light was showing through the blinds, and the birds sang loudly through her open bedroom window. As she sat on the edge of the bed she thought of the white horse with the pink whiskers and the man who brought her the special dream gift.

"Yes, my love," she thought. "I will nurture the dream that I hold in my heart. I will feed it every day and exercise the gift. And even though you are no longer present to cheer me on, I know you watch and clap and hold me close, that I may fulfill all my days and my dreams."

"Let's ride."

Margaret Honnold writes based on her life as a nurse, Alzheimer's caregiver, widow and mother. Her spiritual gift of encouragement takes the form of a blog, essays, poetry, speaking and photography. She has spent time since retirement "Finding Maggie," traveling, and caring for her three beloved Basset Hounds. Find her on maggiehonnold.net.

HIS STORY

By Stephanie Pravata

Once upon a time

In a world gone wrong.

There was only one man

To which the world belonged.

He tried to set things straight.

He tried to make them right.

But all the world was doing

Was putting up a fight.

With each other

One another,

With the man that came to be.

The one and only Messiah

Brought down to save me.

Save everyone from the corruption

And the evil of this place.

Satan tried to brainwash.

Jesus said "back away.

These are my people

They're the reason why I'm here.

I have come to save them before the end of time is near."

At the time of Jesus' crucifixion

Some still did not care.

That He was the Son of Man come down

But this I'm willing to share.

He saves those who seek to know

Who He is and who He was

And if you want to be saved,

You need only ask because.

He'll give you the freedom

And the wisdom to learn

About the world and those around you,

This is knowledge you will yearn-for,

Read your Bible

Keep the good in your heart.

Those are the things that will set you apart

From everyone else.

And then everyone will see

That this man named Jesus

Lives in you and me.

You're a changed person

Reborn with a new love.

A new heart, a new faith

Gifts to you from up above.

His story isn't over.

The bible says He will be back.

Until then you share the good word.

It's the gospel people lack.

I AM MY BELOVED'S AND MY BELOVED IS MINE
(Song of Solomon 6:3)

By Holly T. Ashley

I remember that day very well. I had been through so much and my friend had brought me to meet a boy that she knew from church.

He was also her boyfriend's best friend.

As we walked towards the grassy field I looked at the array of sweaty young men who had just finished a hard game of volley ball. They were hot... yes, yes they were, especially that one... Right. There.

The year was 1987 and we were twenty-something. He was big and strong with dark hair that had been bleached at the tips giving him that buff-surfer look.

At least I hoped that was him.

I wasn't given any description; I was just told that there was this really nice guy... volleyball at the park... and frankly another lonely night at home was not what I needed.

I stood next to my friend taking in the smell of the sweat and the wet grass, as she introduced each boy to me.

But my ears lingered on his name.

David.

Just like the boy of the Bible, he was fearless, handsome and most definitely had my full attention, especially as he stood up and took my hand to properly introduce himself.

"So you're Linda's friend."

A statement so matter of fact, spoken in a deep voice full of confidence, threw me off my game and I stood speechless. I think he got a head nod.

Two years of dating and he continued to make my heart skip beats and could catch my attention with one glance into his crystal blue eyes through the most crowed of rooms.

When he proposed the following year, how I could I possibly say no?

We were inseparable. His parents loved me. He loved me.

I had never felt love like that.

Sweet, adoring, compassionate, unconditional and not just from David, but his parents as well! They were unbelievably loving. I had never seen family done like that.

So I did what any woman would do. I ran.

After all my mother told me, "it will never last."

Leaving my beloved at the proverbial alter, with the beautiful ring he had purchased for me… I just had to go.

Somewhere rooted in my heart and whispers from my mother's voice rang in my ears… "He's too good to be true." Somehow, I knew that if he ever realized how much more he deserved, he would most surely dump me and therefore my heart would be broken.

So I gave the ring back to him and told him goodbye.

He cried.

No. He wept.

For a few months he would show up at my work or at my house.

So I moved.

Not just down the street either. I moved over the Pacific Ocean to the island of Maui where I thought I would find paradise.

For David, life moved forward. It was the twenty-fifth wedding anniversary of his wonderful parents a few months after my departure. So he sold my beautiful wedding ring to his father who, in turn, gave it to his beautiful bride as a gift on that special day.

Life goes on.

Hearts break, people let you down, but no matter what, the world just keeps spinning.

After living on the beautiful island of Maui watching the whales play with dolphins from my condo's window... I came to realize that life on an island is nothing more than glorified isolation, so I came back home.

But not before I tried my hand at another marriage with a child... I soon realized that I had made a terrible mistake.

I ran to David's house as soon as I got home to the mainland.

I knew he still must love me! And I was sure he would love my son. He was so beautiful and David's mother loved babies... I never dreamed he would slam the door in my face.

Yet the world continued to spin.

After my divorce and another move... this time to California to pursue an acting and modeling career, I received notice that I was cast in a very popular television show... and it was filmed back home! I was heading home!

Soon after my arrival, I was notified, the show was cancelled. But I was home, so I did what I always did when I was scared, lonely and afraid... I stopped by to see my friend, David.

David had gotten married.

I stared at the picture of her on his desk. The photo of her was adorable. She was laying on the floor with her arm tucked up underneath her, and her hand holding up her pretty blonde hair.

She was beautiful. Her family was a friend of David's father. They were missionaries in another country. So of course, David and his new bride moved five years after their marriage to join her family.

He finally got what he deserved. A beautiful, loving, Christian woman who would care for him and love him as God defines in His Word.

I did not cry. As a matter of fact, I was so happy for David that he was finally happy that I moved on. For a year I chose not to date, but to pray about my future husband. I was intentional about who I was praying for- from the inside-out. I knew I wanted a man after God's own heart. A man who was strong, sturdy and rugged. He had to be at least 6' tall and very masculine. He had to have a wicked sense of humor and love his mother.

I prayed for him every night.

I set the bar high.

And then I got married.

I chose not to live in the hot, desert dryness of my home state. I wanted to raise my children in the Bible belt where there were changes in the season- like actually four season not just hot and hotter.

I felt that moving my children to a small town might give them more opportunity to grow and thrive. I also thought that it would bring us out of the clutches of my husband's overbearing mother and his addictions to drugs and alcohol.

But it did not.

As my daughter and I were cleaning out a cabinet one day, not realizing what was in a box labeled, "Holly's memories," my daughter proceeded to open it.

The contents spilled out and memories of better days flooded my soul.

I couldn't help but smile through the tears of those college-camps where my friend Linda and I had ransacked someone's cabin and filled their bed with broken eggs… or when I sang in the talent competition for the first time and didn't choke, but actually was asked by the worship leader to join their ensemble.

So many memories. Good memories of happy times, good friends and Godly fellowship.

"Who's this mom?"

My daughter broke my trance as I took a worn out and somewhat bent picture of David, he was kneeling beside the wheel well of his Camaro, next to him was his friend Brian.

I smiled. I remember that day. We were on way to youth camp. David was one of the leaders, often dressing up like Dana Carvey's Church Lady – He was amazing with improve and his knowledge of the Bible stopped everybody in their tracks!

On our way up to the camp we had a flat tire after which, the boys were so proud of their tire-changing abilities, of course I had to take their picture.

"Mom?" Jordyn said raising her Jr. High eyebrows.

"Oh," I slightly laughed but quickly caught myself.

"He's the one that go away, baby." I said, staring into that picture. "They were so proud of themselves," I thought to myself as I put the picture back into the memory album.

I hadn't thought of David in years. But suddenly I wondered how his life had turned out. Mine was certainly a mess. Maybe another move might help? Maybe my mother-in-law could help him overcome his addictions to drugs, alcohol…

And women.

It was my son's senior year when we moved to Texas. My husband's promise of being in his home state with family nearby would be good for the family soon fizzled into an all-out war zone.

Finished playing second fiddle to my husband's addictions, third fiddle to the other women and forth fiddle to his mother, we had to move on. So we came full circle. The final move. Back to where we started.

Divorced again. I thought that would be the worst of my problems until I got fired from my job after using every last penny that my daughter and I had on our new living space, right about that time my daughter, now a high school senior decided that she was going to push me over the edge.

Back in our home town, where bad influences mixed with the hormones of a teenage girl and the perimenopause erratic moods of a wounded, angry, and bitter mother… things were not a happy place.

But as I settled into our new condo with nothing more than a Bible and a queen size bed, I committed myself to reach new heights and forget past hurts and with a firm hand on my daughter we moved forward. One… single… baby step at a time.

Being in the healthcare and fitness field for most of my life I had no choice but to play the cards that had been dealt to me. And as I thumbed through my computer's listing of contacts, I began making some calls and before I knew it, God had me right back on track.

Starting out on a new adventure late into my forties might not have been a great plan for every woman, but God let me know that he was right by my side. I determined that all I needed was Jesus. That He was my sustenance, my all in all.

Oh, my daughter was a handful, no doubt. I took steps to insure she was right where she needed to be at all times, but I knew she was lacking in a good solid male role model. After all, look at what she grew up with and even though you would think that she would learn, she was bringing home these same type of boys.

You know the kind, they don't speak, and they don't want to come into the house, they are apparently opposed to the shower or infatuated with their new hair growth on their face and are proud to show off their miss-matched patches of fur.

"And you want to take my daughter where…?"

"OH…. You don't have a plan…?"

"Goodnight," closing the door, "Bye-Bye."

"MOM!"

I began to put together health and wellness expos and while planning my largest event of the year I knew I was going to need some help. So as I searched the internet to put together my team of everyone from fitness professionals to Dementia lock down facilities, my racing, and excited heart came to a dead stop when his face popped up on my screen.

David.

What was he doing in Arizona…? Wow. He looked fantastic! And his wife!

Wait a minute? That's not his wife… or what I remember as being his wife…. I thought, "Who is that?" Not out of jealousy or anything like that, I just didn't think she looked like the woman I remembered – "Anyway…. This is fantastic!" I thought. So I clicked on David's picture and asked him to "friend" me.

And I waited…. And waited…

The health expo planning was going great, everything was moving into place and then, out of the blue… I got a call from David.

"I've got 30 minutes in between clients. Can you meet me at 4:30?"

Looking at my watch and knowing I had to land this assignment, I said, "Absolutely! I'll be there!"

And there we sat.

It was all business. I knew I only had thirty minutes and I spewed health, fitness, expo… all over his desk! He was polite and calm.

Just like I remembered… but something was most definitely missing.

Where that was wicked sense of humor? He wasn't even smiling.

I didn't even have time to sit back and settle my thoughts before he slid the contract back across the desk and said, "Yeah. It's just not going to happen."

I was shocked. "What?! This was his livelihood! Ever since I've know you…" I thought…. "You eat, drink, breathe, and sleep health and fitness!"

Deep breath.

I did take a deep breath. The first since I had walked in that place. And then I sat back and looked at him. There was a definite difference. This wasn't David. Not my David. My friend of a lifetime, the man after God's own heart, big rugged, mountain of strength… No, this was only a shell of that man.

"You look like you've been run over by a train." I said bluntly, "What has happened to you?"

Since the first time I walked through the doors, he looked relaxed… he even smiled. "Is it that bad?"

"Yep," I remarked, as I gazed at the marquee on his computer screen, "I killed Jesus" it said. I had to shake my head… "Jesus got down off that tree, you know…" I said with a smile.

David went on to tell me about the sham of a "ministry" that took place over seas and after a ruthless divorce he came back home to the states to literally fall apart.

The woman in the picture was most definitely the latest of the great mistakes that he was trying to deal with… Yes, he was one big hot mess that was for sure.

So I walked out the door that day, praying for my friend. My heart breaking over the mess that he had made in his life and the un-forgiveness that he had for himself.

I realized that we are all just one big "hot mess" and if we weren't then Jesus would have never had to hang on that tree at all.

I came home and sat down at my computer, determined to complete the tasks required of me to put on this gigantic health expo and just as I started my search for a new director of fitness, in walked my daughter…

Another boy had trampled on her heart and she blamed God. "Mom, you just don't get it," was the usual answer, so I decided that she was right and to bypass it all together with some great news!

"You're right, I don't get it… I obviously don't understand men… why would I think that I could possibly understand boys, but I know someone who does. And he's a personal trainer!"

I did understand parenthood and that it required both a positive female and a male role model and – I knew exactly what male to I was going to contact.

The next week my daughter met with David, "The one that got away" she thought that was pretty funny and felt an immediate connection. The training schedule had begun and she was going through David's workout program 30 minutes a day, 3 times per week.

She was so thrilled. No really, she was! She and David hit it off perfectly and Dave was able to counsel her about boys, she had her confidant, and the workouts removed the carb-loaded emotional eating residue, and that lifted her self-esteem.

All was good.

One night after leading a support group at a very large church, I was standing in the parking lot talking to one of my attendees when I heard a very familiar voice behind me. I smiled as I turned to shock David with my cheesy grin and loud "Well, hello there!"

After we realized that we both lead a group there on that particular night, we bumped into each other every week.

I began to understand more of what his torrential home life was like and he let me know his mother had been undergoing treatments for cancer for the past 4 years.

I began to realize how to pray for David… or so I thought.

A few months after our first chance meeting at the church, David told me that his mom was back in the hospital with another spot of cancer. Trying to be positive, I told David that this might be what God uses to re-unite the broken family and that maybe his wife would finally have something to do with this wonderful family and all would work out.

Not so much.

Apparently, the wife wanted nothing to do with David, his family, his church or him for that matter.

I was dumbfounded to say the least. I asked how a woman could be so brutal, and found out more than I bargained for – David was in a very volatile, abusive relationship.

I most certainly knew what that was all about. So all I could do was pray for my friend.

I asked how I should pray for him and said to "pray that God would get the glory no matter what happened."

A few weeks later my daughter graduated high school and moved to Texas to go to school and live out her dreams.

Alone again. But I was fine with that. I had my little condo, my thriving marketing firm, I was even teaching support groups and even fitness groups on the side. All was well.

With me anyway. I had no idea about David.

After I heard about his mom and then his home life I was distraught. Maybe it was because my daughter had opted for the wife-cheating drunk of an ex-husband that she thought she could "save," and I felt alone and abandoned. But my heart broke for my friend and I would inadvertently show up at the church he attended…. Find myself looking at his webpages and following his every word on social media… holy cow! What was I doing!

"OMG! I'm spiritually stalking him!" I thought!

So I stopped.

I went back to my happy home life and solitude of being over forty and fabulous! I loved my beautiful condo, my friends, my church and my life. Things were finally getting back on track with me emotionally and I was enjoying the "splendor of solitude!" As I called it.

Then my phone rang…

It was a text message.

From David.

"I'm done. Just wanted you to know. I'm moving today, my kids are coming to visit and it won't be at this house – gotta go…. Using this time to find a storage unit…"

I stared at the message for a while… my mind racing to catch up with what I was reading.

I typed, "You don't need a storage unit… I have an empty 2 car garage… you're in a hurry… just move it here…" Then I pressed send….

And waited.

And then I put the phone down.

But just as I did, a message came in: "Really! That would be awesome! I'll be there after work!"

I went numb.

"What just happened?" I thought… "What…. Now…?"

Well, I'm learning not to ask those questions anymore. I remember when I made the decision to move to Arizona and start life over again, God told me through a time of Bible reading that He was going to show up in a big way… "More than we could ever hope for or imagine…"

And He has.

Who would have thought that twenty-five years would come and go until paths would cross in such a way as to re-unite two people who had loved so each other so much for so long.

After David's kids finished their visit with their father, David moved in with his parents and we picked up where we left off over twenty-five years earlier.

We were married eight months afterward and his mom and dad stood up for us as David's mentor presided over the wedding. All agreed that we had to get married... that it couldn't, shouldn't wait... due to the fact that God had a plan for us twenty-five years ago and we needed to get moving on it before we died.

David's mom passed away that following October but not before purchasing my birthday present, that David's dad found buried in the closet of their 6-week-old home.

She had bought me a new set of mixing bowls – how she knew that I would decorate my kitchen in red and white was beyond me... but somehow she knew.

But the best gift of all was buried at the bottom of the set.

In its own little box lay my engagement ring from so very long ago... A gift from my in-laws and from God, letting us all know that everything had come full circle.

Holly T. Ashley is a published author, professional speaker, writer, and founder of R3. Redemption. Restoration. Recovery. Domestic Violence Services and Training. David Ashley, aka: The Pastor of Pump is the founder of Cross Strength Ministries, LLC and is the founder of Fitness by Design and holds a Master's degree in Apologetics and his Masters of Divinity. He is an Evangelist, speaker, writer, and personal trainer.

OTHERIZE

By Patricia Miller

How is it we manage to 'otherize'

those we don't agree with

those who we think are wrong, or

make us angry?

It's easy to categorize or

'otherize'.

It means I'm okay, and

you're not.

I'm Loved, and, too bad,

you're not.

These are some of

our current 'otherizes":

those with Trump,

those with Hillary,

those who are Catholic,

those who are Protestant,

those who are right-wing,

those who are left-wing,

those who are black,

those who are white,

those who are Jewish,

those who are Muslin,

those who are Hindu,

those who are gay,

those who are straight,

those who carry guns,

those who don't carry guns.

There are a thousand ways

to 'otherize' others,

to put them in a box.

We do it all the time.

The key issue is to know

that, regardless of our 'otherizing',

we are all in this world

together.

Because I disagree with you,

I'm not wrong or right.

Because you disagree with me,

you are not wrong or right.

It just means we disagree,

that's all.

It takes honesty with self

to see that, at one time or another,

we have all lied, cheated,

been dishonest in one way or another.

To 'fess up' to this truth

It to have compassion for self, and

then have compassion for others.

It takes forgiveness of self, to know we

are forgiven, and then we can forgive others.

And, ultimately,

we can be friends, not enemies,

and know we are all

one in the Spirit.

Patricia "Trish" Miller is on this adventure we call Life. So far, she has discovered that "God is always with us to cast out all fear ----of other people, other religions, others who look and act differently, and those who hurt us, whom we can't forgive. God is continually telling us, I am the Center of your life; don't be distracted by all that is going on about you; don't be swayed by the emotions of the crowd, the media, the politicians, the world situation; hold fast to Me; stay with Me in the Center; know that I am with you always." From Fresh Breezes Blow, *by Patricia J. Parker-Miller. She is a listener, a singer, an author, and a Mom. She lives in Albuquerque, New Mexico with her daughter, Diane. She can be reached at trish1936@gmail.com*

[The word, "Otherize", is borrowed from Dr. Christena Cleveland.]

SHINING YOUR LIGHT BRIGHTER THAN BEFORE

By Misty Thompson

I recently spent a weekend in Sedona, Arizona where I did some fall cleaning of my soul. Before the weekend started, I was anxious and nervous about what was about to happen to me. I knew that something magnificent was in the works for me and as I reflect back to the last three days, my expectation of my weekend was only about one-fourth of what it actually was.

As most people know, the energy in Sedona is massive. It showed itself to me in different ways. The people, the scenery, the air, and the actual ground. My body was completely in awe by the whole stimulation that Sedona conveyed. My ears are still buzzing after being home a day and I found that feeling to be comforting. The skin on my face from being touched is still so sensitive and the thought of that energy I experienced still amazes me and make me weak with satisfaction. I have experienced self-care in the past, but this is truly what the term self-care really means and I do love it.

My weekend involved several exercises that heightened each of our awareness of not only our own need to shed those stale covers that suffocate our true self from shining, but also allowing us to see the potential within ourselves that we may never have seen before on our own. It was a time to not only connect with other like-minded people but also realizing that our lives were intermingled in a past life and this was our opportunity to find resolution. As each of our experience was different, we were all there for many similar reasons and that was to unlock those blocks that we had upon ourselves and to let our light shine brighter than before our arrival.

I was able to see the potential I have within myself and to reach the goals I never thought I would have for myself. Knowing that my loved ones who have passed are with me and believe in me is a definite validation that there is more to my life than being ordinary, like I thought before Sedona. That is extremely comforting as I know that I am not only guided by them, but I know that I have the Archangels on my side encouraging me even though I may not always feel it.

As I became comfortable at the creek, I sat on a massive rock and I felt the sun radiating on my face. I was soaking in the familiar light that I had been missing in my life for so long. The intoxicating and rhythmic sound of the flowing water invited me to leave my cares and concerns with it so it could be taken away. As I became more and more comfortable, I thanked the waters for this amazing gift. If I tried to explain my involvement to those closest to me, I do not know if I would be able to find the exact words that would convey the feelings that I was experiencing as it was massive. I released the guilt, shame, frustration and allowed myself to forgive myself and others. The creek and it's healing water is more than willing to take on my cares, as it understands the greater good in order for the light and love of the higher source to envelope me entirely with love. The knowing that all is well and that my God believes in me gives me confidence that I too am now able to believe in myself and I accept all of me. I will no longer allow anyone's judgments, not even my own judgment, affect me and I will now let my light shine for the world to see.

I could feel the vibration of the drum and hear the beat pulsating in the background which invited those negative ego based emotions to be released so that my core self can be comfortably and completely seen. I thanked Mother Earth for her healing and I will continue to be grateful of her understanding, for her love, and for her healing. I touched the cold, breathtaking water with my hand as I imagined, those heavy and dense emotions race out of my head and out of my heart through my left arm and out of my left hand into the water. I also, picked up a small stone and as I gripped it tightly in my hand, I imagined those negative ego based emotions being imprinted onto that stone. I concentrated intently as I threw that stone into the water. As an offering, I gave the water some sage to show how grateful I was for its help. I realized in that moment that I am incredibly blessed.

It has always been difficult for me to stand in my own truth. As I am sure others who are finding their path have experienced the same feelings. I have always felt fearful of being judged for one reason or another. I have had family members, who have claimed to be religious, who look down on my spiritual studies and make jokes about my teachings on Angels. I have had people tell me that I wear my emotions on my sleeve and that showing my emotions can be a sign of weakness. Deep down I knew that was wrong, but I still believed others instead of following my own light. My weekend in Sedona reminded me that I do not need to care about anyone else, only my true self. I know that everyone dances to their own music and I truly do not care which music anyone in my family dances to. All I care about is that they are comfortable with their own dance.

Making a connection with those involved with the retreat is a great way to see your own abilities. It is incredibly astonishing to be in an environment where everyone is helping each other and there are no insecurities amongst each other. It was my experience that there was continued support for each other and our talents were validated and not imprisoned. In the past, with those who I thought were supportive of me, my beliefs, and my dreams, I would experience eyes rolling, snide comments, and judgmental whispering. Now because of my weekend experience, I do not worry nor care about those insignificant stories because I have come to realize that I am not my story, and so it is.

I am extremely grateful beyond words for the experience that Sedona has brought to me, for me, through me, and with me as it has allowed me to shine my light brighter than I ever imagined.

Misty Proffitt-Thompson, is a Certified Angel Card Reader and a Mind, Body, Spirit Practitioner who has her own spiritually based business named Mystified Enlightenment. Misty is a contributing author for the book, The Peace Makers: Restoring Love in the World through Stories of Compassion and Wisdom and is currently working on a book about the tragic death of her sister and the spiritual connection between the two of them.

WHOSE YOU ARE

By Wyshika L. Gibson

You are a child of the living God

You are a son or a daughter of a King

Your worth is more than man eyes can see

Your value is measured by God alone

You are loved more than you know

You are fearfully and wonderfully made

You are created in God's marvelous image

You are set a part to represent him

You are set free by the Son indeed

You are blessed

You are rooted in God's word like a green bay tree

You are planted by the streams

You are shaped for HIS glory

You are not ashamed of the dirt that continues to help you flourish

You are a new creature in Christ Jesus

You are comfortable in your skin

You are not your past

You are an overcomer

You are redeemed by the Lord and called HIS own

You are a part of God's wonderful plan

You are seated with him in heavenly realms

You know your worth

You know who and whose you are

You know whom you belong to

GHOSTS OF LAKESIDE INN

By R.D. Petti

The first time you open a window after six months of air conditioning running nonstop, you know autumn has arrived in Florida. To newcomer transplants from northern climes, the change in season is almost imperceptible, but to a 30-year resident like Judy Birdsong, the transition to fall was downright exhilarating. Judy had an avid interest in all things supernatural. She looked forward each year to celebrating the autumn festivals of remembrance—Samhain, Dia de los Muertos, and All Hallows' Eve, to name a few—the time of year when the veil is thin between the world of the living and the realm of the dead.

This year to observe the day of remembrance of those loved ones who have crossed over to the other side, Judy traveled from her home in Tampa to Mount Dora to stay with her friend, Sam, and attend a ceremony Sam's group was holding on October 31st. Judy initially turned down Sam's invitation; she wasn't up for the drive. Then, at the last minute, she decided to go. Besides, the ceremony might be healing for her.

Judy had lost her mother earlier that year, and her father had transitioned several years before. After her father passed, she took in her mother to care for her. Judy's mother made it difficult for anyone to love her. Her end of life was no different. Her mother had taken center stage all her life; the other family members were her supporting cast. She remained a diva to her death, making her grand exit with a massive stroke. When her mother died, Judy was relieved more than saddened. Emotionally numb and physically exhausted from tending to the histrionic demands of her mother, Judy never really had the opportunity to grieve the loss of her beloved father. The ceremony would give her permission to do so.

"After lunch, I'll show you around town. We've got time before the ghost tour starts," Sam said to Judy. Sam had purchased tickets to the ghost walk for the day before the ceremony knowing how much Judy relished the paranormal. The tour started at sundown at the Lakeside Inn by Lake Dora.

They had lunch at a tea house in the historic district and then took a stroll up and down the hilly side streets of the district. At a pleasant 70 degrees, the air held just the suggestion of crispness.

"Why is this place called Mount Dora?" Judy asked. "There are no mountains."

"I guess the founders had a sense of humor. Mount Dora has the rare distinction in flat Florida of being situated on a plateau some 184 feet above sea level," Sam explained. "In addition to the prominent lake, Lake Dora, there are many other lakes and hills in this area. Mount Dorians say it reminds them of New England."

They walked all over town. The live oak trees draped with Spanish moss cast long shadows in the autumnal afternoon sun. They decided to go to the Lakeside Inn early to explore it before the walking tour began. They approached the inn from the back and meandered around the side of the building to the front.

"I can see why this is on the ghost walk. It's definitely haunted," Judy observed.

"How do you know?"

"The building makes my skin crawl. I get that sensation when I'm in a haunted place." Judy studied the yellow hotel with the long, white verandah and green awning. She surveyed the grounds leading to Lake Dora, the manicured gardens, and gazebo. "This is going to sound weird, but think I've been here before. This place looks very familiar."

They entered the dark, Victorian lobby of the inn. The presence of the spectral guests sent chills down Judy's spine. She was transported back to when they were alive and staying at the hotel. In her mind's eye, she could see them enjoying dinner in the dining room, playing the piano, and sitting by the fire on a chilly Florida night. She could also envision herself back in time on another visit to this hotel. "This place is giving me the creeps. Let's go back outside."

Judy couldn't shake the sense that she had been here before. *Was I ever in Mount Dora?* They followed a sidewalk past some cottages and a building with hotel rooms alongside the main hotel to Lake Dora. The lake conjured memories of another place and time, of Judy's childhood haunts on the lake by her New England home—whiling away long summer afternoons swimming in its cool waters, hiking in its painted woods on a cool autumn day, shoveling snow from the ice to skate until the early darkness of a winter night crept in, and exploring its rivulets and streams among trees flaunting their new growth of spring leaves. Despite her codependent childhood, Judy was always happy when near the lake.

The inn and the lake evoked another memory, long dormant but not forgotten. "This place reminds me of a hotel my parents and I visited when we first moved to Florida, after I graduated from college. The hotel was beside a lake and also had a separate building like this one." That trip, she remembered, had been unusual, and had fostered an uncharacteristic tenderness in her. The hotel had been magical, casting a spell on her mother. It had removed the mask of the impossible-to-please critic, revealing the fragile, gentle woman previously hidden to her daughter, a woman who was accepting, caring, and validating. She was all about Judy.

For this one enchanting interlude, Judy was touched by her mother's love, becoming a child again held in invisible maternal arms, and her heart was comforted.

"I remember I stayed in a room in the building alongside the main hotel. The room next to mine was haunted. I spent the night—all night—listening to banging pipes in the room adjoining mine and repeated sounds of the toilet flushing. I believe the spirit there thoroughly enjoyed keeping me awake all night playing the pipes in the bathroom."

"Could it be the same hotel?" Sam asked.

"I don't know. That would be hard to believe, but it's possible," Judy replied.

"Strange," Sam said. "Others are gathering for the tour; let's join them."

****

The memories of the hotel visit with her parents haunted Judy the rest of All Hallows' Eve weekend in Mount Dora. The ceremony of remembrance was particularly poignant. The recollection of her mother during that stay rekindled the embers of love in Judy's heart for her. At the same time, Judy was filled with a profound regret and sadness that they had missed an entire lifetime of not being able to express that love.

She remembered she had taken a memento of the hotel they had visited to cherish the sweet time with her parents, small bottles of shampoo and conditioner that bore the name of the hotel on their labels. She had tucked them away for many years but they always remained a coveted reminder of the visit. The memory of the place may have faded but not the tenderness of the stay. *When I go home, I'm going to find those bottles. This is too crazy to be a coincidence.*

As soon as she arrived home, she searched for the toiletries long packed away. The label on the bottles would confirm the name. She combed through drawers, cabinets, and cupboards. She looked in containers, bags, and boxes that she hadn't opened in years. She found a bag of odds and ends under the bathroom sink, dumped the contents on the floor, and picked up the bottles. She turned them around and read the labels. *How is this possible?*

What prompted Judy at the last minute to go to Mount Dora that particular weekend and visit a place that would raise the ghosts of her past? Was it chance? Was it pure coincidence that she ended up at an inn that would dust off the cobwebs of a time hidden in the shadows of her mind, bringing into focus a glimpse of her mother that would infuse her numb heart with tenderness and allow her to grieve? Or could it have been orchestrated by an eternal heart—now open in unconditional love—that reached out to her when the veil is thin between the worlds of the living and the dead?

R.D. Petti is a mystic, poet, and debut author of the spiritual fantasy, Nettie's Tea House: A Tale of the Afterlife. The novel has been acclaimed by a Writer's Digest contest judge as "a rewarding tale, meant to be savored." Having earned a B.A. in English Literature and an M.A. in Counseling Psychology, she has been a lifelong student of consciousness, seeking the knowledge and wisdom found in mystery and spiritual traditions. She has served as a mental health counselor, hospice volunteer, and Reiki Master Practitioner. Ms. Petti resides in Sarasota, Florida. She is a Letters member of the National League of American Pen Women and belongs to the ABC Artisans of Books. Her poem, Reflections on a Passing, was awarded first place in the 2015 Poetry Writing Contest and has been published by the Spiritual Writers Network in its poetry anthology, Illuminations of the Soul. An environmental enthusiast, Ms. Petti supports the Mote Marine Laboratory as a volunteer.

Connect with R.D. Petti

Website: www.rdpetti.com

Social Media: www.facebook.com/rdpettiauthor

CIRCLE OF DOORS

By Pamela Sears

The corridor is long

From beginning to end

And along the way

Are choices within

Each door holds a place

An idea, a thought

Of which way to turn

Take this one or not?

No matter which door

One decides to choose

All have a place

With nothing to lose

In choosing one door

The path then unfolds

And then there will come

another door to behold

and so it's a circle

Each door will be met

At the appointed time

Perhaps all preset

So worry not

Which choices you make

For all will be opened

And none will you forsake

Let go of fear

Let go of doubt

Embrace each choice

With a smile and a shout

For at least you have chosen

And moved forward you see

You didn't stand still

And that sets you free

Pam Sears *is a Licensed Massage Therapist , Bodyworker, and a Psychic Medium. Her book of Poetry called Whispers of the White Dove will be published in January of 2017.*

Website: pamsears.com

FESTIVE FUN AND A FABULOUS NEW YEAR

By Tonia Browne

This chapter invites you to examine your *manual for life*. Did you write it yourself or are you following someone else's? Is it still right for you or does it need editing?

As 2016 comes to a close give yourself a gift. Look afresh at your own specific manual for life and rewrite it to make sure it still fits, reflecting who you are and who you want to be.

Pardon?

"Father Christmas!" he whispered.

I just stared.

"Father Christmas!" he repeated into my ear.

It wouldn't have mattered how many times he had said it, I would still have felt clueless about how I was meant to respond. What did he want me to do? I was at a loss. I knew I was meant to do something, but what was it?

I might have been very concerned by now if my mother hadn't been standing in the corner of the room. She was looking at me as if it was perfectly normal for a man in a white coat to whisper funny things in my ear. I remembered her talking to me before about strange men. At that time she told me not to talk to them and certainly not to get into a car or walk off with them.

I was not sure how I was meant to take the man who towered over me. It was April and he was whispering in my ear about Santa. If I had not been a child of six years old but an adult, I think I would have told him not to be so silly and walked out of the room. I was not. I was a child who had been taught to respect her elders.

"Father Christmas! " he said again.

With his red face and his white coat I was wondering if he thought I had mistaken him for Father Christmas. Did he think me a fool? I knew he was a doctor because we were in a hospital and I was also well aware that my mother thought I was deaf.

"Father Christmas!" he said, one last time.

He then backed away from me and in his normal voice he asked me if I knew what he had said.

"Yes!" I replied.

"Well, what did I say?" he asked.

"You said Father Christmas!" I said.

The doctor looked at me and then at my mother. He then shared his verdict that I was not deaf and that I heard very well indeed.

"She just doesn't want to answer!" he added.

"What a cheek!" I remember thinking.

I would have happily answered him, but he had not asked a question. I had no idea that an answer was expected. I had been waiting for an instruction.

The Instruction

I realise now, I have probably been waiting for an instruction about how to live for most of my life.

That's not exactly true. There were many manuals out there, but they never seemed to be easy to follow. I guess what I wanted was something that I could understand and went at my pace. I wanted a manual that was written just for me.

As I began my journey into self-development I was guided to reflect on my inner belief system. Whether I realised it or not, I had a set of instructions that were there in the conscious and unconscious parts of my brain. When I discovered my instructions didn't work for me, I was invited to question where they had come from. This was a huge breakthrough. Who would have thought I was responding to my life from a set of instructions that I didn't approve of, didn't write and that didn't work for me. It didn't really bode well for living an authentic life!

To live in harmony with myself I knew it was time to go back to the spiritual library and get a new manual.

The Exchange

I had always felt out of sync with my own life. "What do you want to be when you grow up?" I was often asked. "I want to be happy!" was my usual reply. "No, what job do you want?"

I had always felt that the job didn't really matter if you were happy. Perhaps I never really understood the question. Or perhaps they didn't really understand my answer.

It was not that I was unhappy. It was just that I always thought there was a more intense sense of happiness waiting for me around the corner. It was that feeling I wanted to *be* when I was older. Now there are courses on how to be happy and the value of happiness seem main stream.

The Manual

As I learnt more about self-development, I dug out that child's desire to be happy once more. I placed it in the centre of my new manual.

It was during this time that I acknowledged the benefits of designing my own ever-changing manual, one thought at a time.

If we are more conscious about bringing our beliefs and values onto the table, we can look at them more closely. We can also think about whether we still agree with them. We can then create a more tailored manual to meet our uniqueness.

We can use ideas from our past and from others if they fit, but we do so in a more conscious way. It is our life experiences and the lessons we learn on our journey that make these instructions more real to us.

I have been on many courses, read many books and listened to many speakers. The people who resonated the best and for the longest were those who offered suggestions and shared their reasoning. They were in a place where they knew their ideas worked for them, but they also appreciated that their manual could not be passed on in its entirety to someone else.

Festive Fun

If my manual had been consciously designed by myself earlier in life, I might have giggled at the age of six when the man in the white coat whispered the words "Father Christmas" in my ear. I am sure that this more spontaneous reaction to his whispers would have lightened the mood and it might have altered the conclusion of the doctor himself. It was not that I did not *want* to answer. It was that I did not know *how* he wanted me to answer.

At that time, my unacknowledged manual directed me to wait for the instruction and then aim to give the answer that would please.

On-Line, Ever Changing Creation

I believe that much of the fun and reward in life comes from continuously designing and redesigning your own manual and making sure it supports you as you change. This realisation was another huge break through for me.

Our manuals can be more like on-line ebooks or websites. We can keep editing and refining them to suit our changing thoughts, ideas, situations and experiences. They then become less like printed documents and more like pieces of artwork in progress. You then can play more consciously in this amazing universe as a co-creator of creation.

A Fabulous New Year

As this year closes and the next opens, I gift myself the opportunity to once again explore my manual. I will edit out any pieces that no longer work for me and paint over them with flair, colour and with the intention of making this New Year a better experience for myself and those around me.

Who will join me?

Tonia Browne *is a bestselling author, teacher and coach.*

Tonia is a strong advocate of inviting fun into our lives and encouraging people to see their world from a new perspective. She has received support from amazing people on her journey and enjoys returning the favour by assisting others in their development.

As a teacher, Tonia has worked in the United Kingdom and internationally for over twenty years and was an Assistant Head for seven. She is a Heal Your Life® Workshop Leader, Coach and Business Trainer.

Tonia is the author of SPIRITUAL SEAS: Diving into Life. This book describes her diving adventures and how the sea provided opportunities for spiritual and personal growth. In this book you will discover how one person used a range of strategies to overcome the challenges of her early childhood, rediscovered her place in the universe and turned her life around.

Connect with her at toniabrowne.com.

TUG OF WAR –
SHIFT OF REALITY

By Bonnie Larson

Reality shifts to majority,

Of love, light, prosperity.

Not a tug-of-war or force

Not either… or, of course.

No fists of war, appeal to hearts,

Yes, arm in arm, the place to start.

Majority rules like shifting sands,

But love, joining of hands,

Holding light with all our might,

Safe harbor, freedom sight.

No fear or force, shift to Source,

Faith and confidence seeds do sew,

Spiritual way, deeds do show.

Increase our numbers,

No one slumbers.

Raise our hands, count us in,

Believe in Him, He will win.

THE SEARCH FOR I

By Sampson Oak Williams

She searched far and wide,
To find the child inside,
Hidden deep behind a lie,
Herself without the ties.

Who was she?
Who should she be?
Who was she really?

She left no stone unturned,
Examined everything she had learned,
Everything she had burned,
Nothing was clear,
Between everything she held dear,
Everything she did fear.

Then the voice came LOUD,
I will lift your shroud,
You have strings,
Attached to so many things,

Love lost,

Love gained,

Love that cost,

Love that remains,

All of these are yours to keep,

On the surface or down deep,

They are ALL you,

You are everything YOU do,

The lies,

The ties,

The truth,

Lost youth,

Who should you BE?

Be here NOW with me.

Not then,

Not when,

Not soon,

Or tomorrow at noon,

This instant now,

No need to search for how,

You have always been you,

There's nothing you ever had to do.

*About **Sampson Oak Williams** the writer:*

He's married to a former fairy,

Who keeps his life bright and airy,

A Reiki master and father of two,

Lover of trees beer and spirit too,

Marketing exec and shamanic player,

Gentleman poet and life surveyor,

Wants only to entertain and empower you,

To do the best you,

You can do,

Stay tuned for his first book Perspective,

An illustrated inspirational poetry collective.

HOPE

By Dorian Leigh Quillen

In 2010, I was very sick and in the hospital for nearly two months. For someone who was used to being healthy, it was demoralizing to lay day after day in a hospital bed, my movement restricted and my spirits low. The stomach infection I had was very stubborn and after being treated with everything that was supposed to work, I simply wasn't getting better.

One afternoon alone in my room, I began to wonder, "What if I never get out of this, what if this is going to kill me?" Nothing the doctors told me sounded positive or like they even knew what else to do. I found myself losing hope.

At that moment, the door opened and in walked a middle-aged man wearing an Indiana Jones type hat. His face was peaceful and his skin was radiantly smooth. I had never seen him before in my life.

"Hello," he said with a smile. With him, he carried a huge plastic container stuffed with food and other goodies.

I greeted him back, thinking he was probably some volunteer bringing snacks to patients. I was surprised when he told me he wanted me to have the entire container. He said it was full of things that he had already had approved for me by the nurses, and that I could offer it to visitors or family or have it there to eat when I was by myself. Then he said the most interesting thing to me.

"God told me," he said, "to come today to tell the person in this room that they are not to give up hope."

I was momentarily stunned. I said, "Well, that's nice, because it's really easy when you're up here for a long time to lose hope."

He said, "Yes, it is easy to lose hope, but I am telling you – God told me to come today to tell the person in this room that they are not to give up hope."

Our interaction was very short. I thanked him again and drifted off to sleep.

When I awoke, I imagined I had dreamed that some cool looking guy in an awesome hat had come into my room and left me a boatload of goodies. Then I noticed the huge container bursting with snacks on my bedside table.

"Wow," I thought, "that was a real person!"

I didn't get well that day or for many days yet to come. What I did know from then on was that I WAS going to make it out of the illness. It was not going to kill me. I was eventually going to be okay and go home. I had HOPE.

Looking back, I still don't know the identity of my visitor. What I do know is sometimes when we are in our darkest moments, a miracle occurs and brings us back to life in ways that are hard to explain.

I have learned from this to never get so discouraged that I stop believing in miracles. Miracles are real. And they can happen to YOU.

Dorian Leigh Quillen is an award-winning journalist and licensed professional counselor in Oklahoma City. She is the author of "Class Act-Eight Young People Who Turned Tragedy into Triumph" and "Letters From Aunt Dorie."

LEAF WISDOM

By Beth Duncan

A scarlet leaf floats in air,
a gentle ballet of farewell.
As she touches the ground
Mother Earth embraces her,
graces her with warm love.
I am stilled, filled with awe
at this lithesome dance of
death. When I raise my eyes
through bare branches open
to sky, I see blue Heaven.

OK GOD, NOW WHAT?

By Sherry A. Tillman

Lillie and her coworker, Fatima had decided to have lunch outside on the plaza, Freedom Plaza. It was about a five minute walk from their office building on 11th and Pennsylvania Avenue NW. The popular rectangular shaped area was carved out amongst stores, office buildings, restaurants, Federal and District of Columbia government buildings. It was situated between two streets, 13th and 14th Streets.

The sunlight was plentiful. The clear blue hue of the sky, the feel of the sun, and the wispy clouds was relaxing. No matter where anyone sat, Freedom Plaza offered an excellent view of the back of the White House; the Reagan International Building; The Post Office; the Old Post Office Pavilion; The Justice Department; the FBI Building and a picturesque view of the Dome of the Capitol.

For moments of peace, Lillie would often come out and eat lunch by herself. The time alone afforded her a few moments of quiet and to let go of the hectic pace of her work at Blackstone Investments for an hour each day. Fatima, however, wanted to have lunch with Lillie.

"Lillie," Fatima said, "at times when I look at you, you are so deep in thought and I wonder where you are. Are you okay, dear?

"Yeah I am, I guess. I get lost in my thoughts when I think a lot about my faith. I am really ready to grow in my faith and so much so that at times I don't know where to begin. I think because

I don't know where to begin that creates the deep thinking; if that makes any sense."

"Faith just is. It is a belief in something greater than you that operates in your life for your greater good. Are you a believer?" Fatima asked.

"I absolutely am," Lillie said enthusiastically."

"Then I must say to you honestly and forthrightly, there are no two ways about it. You must trust God for everything. You know that can be hard because we live in a world of right now and I gotta do it my way."

"I get it."

"I have to ask, do you know what it means to trust God? I mean for everything!!"

"I am learning?"

"I feel the need to share my story with you."

Fatima had never spoken of where she came from; where she went to school; her parents; siblings; nothing. She stood about 5'10", thin with a smooth, deep, rich, dark, unblemished complexion. Fatima had a long neck and she walked tall and proud. She wore her hair cropped in a curly afro. Fatima was regal and had an air of royalty about her.

"Yes, my story. Faith is an awesome thing for believers. It opens doors that a no man can shut and shuts doors no man can open. God will move mountains for those that believe and have faith that He will provide."

"Oh yeah?"

"Absolutely."

"When I left my native Africa, it was by God's grace. The village my family lived in was a peaceful place. The majority were

Christians. A small number were Muslims. No matter the belief, we respected each other.

"We had a comfortable home. I will never call it a hut because it was home. It was made of mud, twigs, and palm leaves of all kinds, long grass, and reeds. Our home was built by my father. It was large enough that we had two rooms. My siblings and I shared one room and my parents had their own space and then there was the front space which is what you all here call a living room. This served as a meeting place. We ate our meals, prayed, talked, and sang, with each other there.

"My village consisted of several families that had been there for generations; a place where traditions had been passed down through generations. My parents were taught by their parents and so forth. They operated and ran their home as a team.

"Over time, there was talk of extremists moving into our peaceful village. We heard about this from our parents when they thought we were asleep. We respected our parents so much that we followed their lead. We were afraid but dad assured us that things would work out for the greater good.

"Although Dad talked of leaving, he was afraid to leave all that he had known. His fear paralyzed him and his family. The head of our home was afraid to trust the head of his heart and that was God.

"When rumors of the madness gained momentum my father had a plan. He said, '*If anything should happen we will go run and hide in the thick of the brush. We will stay close to one another. Once there, do not move, do not scream. Remain as silent as possible. No matter what you hear or see, please do not say a word.*'

"Early one morning, we heard cries like we had never heard before."

'Get-up, get-up,' my father said. We must leave!'

"We ran out the back of our home unnoticed as fast as we could into the thick brush that was on the outside of our village. My feet met the ground without fail. Sticker Brides scraped my skin and stung like a paper cut. The brush was our only haven against the animals invading our village. The animals in the brush were the least of our worries.

"Father used the light from the moon to count his family. We stayed low until he told us when to move further into the brush. Our movements were swift and hurried.

"From afar, we could see that fires had been set. Plumes of smoke and ash billowed high over the village.

"By daylight, I looked around, my parents and brothers and sisters were gone. I was all alone. I did not make any noise as the brush was my only protection. I held tightly to the bag of food my dad shoved into my hand before we left. I was frightened beyond words, Lillie."

Lillie had long stopped eating her lunch because Fatima's story took her into those woods. She felt as if she was running with Fatima's family into the woods to safety from those who had invaded their village. She imagined Fatima being alone, scared, and separated from my family.

"By nightfall, I took advantage of the light that illuminated from the moon. I had no idea where I was or how far away I was from my village. The stench of death was all around me. I bumped into bodies; fell into pools of blood as I tried finding my way.

"At some point, I began to pray. I asked God to help me. I told God how alone I felt without the protection of my family. I told God I had no understanding of any of this but I would trust His will for my life.

"At some point after I prayed, I fell asleep. I was tucked away under a thick bush. Then all of a sudden from out of nowhere I was hoisted in the air into the arms of some unknown person. I had no idea who he was, or where he was taking me. I kicked and screamed, 'please don't kill me."

"This man held onto me. I begged this stranger to release me; to let me be. He remained quiet and kept walking and loaded me onto a flatbed truck.

He whispered, *'everything is going to be alright.'*

"I did not believe him. I cried until I passed out. When I woke up, I was in a ward of some kind.

The man walked toward me. He said, "I see you have calmed down."

"He sat next to my bed and held my hand. Then this nurse, a white lady, came over to my bed; she looked at me also and said, *"hello."*

"I looked around. I was clean and in a clean bed. My cuts and bruises were bandaged. They brought me food. They insisted that I eat. They looked after me as if I were their own child.

"What was left of the bag of food my dad had given me was right next to my bed. I began to relax.

"The man spoke first, my name is Chukwu and I am a member of the missionary army that came after your village was invaded.

"Have you seen my family; my parents and two brothers and two sisters?"

"*My child,* he says, *I do not know your family. When I found you, you were asleep and snoring. I think it was the snoring that got you noticed."*

"*Please forgive me, I did not mean to scare you. But we entered the brush to reclaim as many villagers as we were able too. You were alone, holding onto your bag. You gave me a fit, and rightfully so, until you passed out. You are safe."*

"Where are my family? We left the village together. I am not certain how I was separated from them. Sir, you have got to help me find my family."

"Lillie, I did not know if the home I had always known was standing. All I did know was that I was safe. I was fed and cared for by the nurse, Sarah and this soldier, Chukwu was always nearby.

"The nurse, Sarah and the African soldier, Chukwu and I became friends. They comforted me in a way that let me know that God was real. I remembered my prayer asking God to keep me. And Lillie he did!

"I was brought out of that horrid mess scared and bruised, but none-the-less, blessed and safe. God's favor is real. In all manner, have faith, that God and God alone will see you through. He will bring the right people in your life at the right time to make sure that all of your needs are met. He will wipe your tears and comfort you. You will be kept you in perfect peace.

"Sarah later became my adoptive mom and brought me back to the States with her. She never stopped looking for my family. Much to my delight, they made it to safety after that horrible night. They eventually made their way to the States being granted asylum as I was. She explained that they had given up hope of ever finding me or that I was even alive. They had no idea how I would survive alone. I asked God to keep my family. And God did!"

Lillie sat there looking at Fatima Adobola. She had no idea that this was her story. Fatima never spoke much about her life prior to coming to the States. There was an accent but not a very thick one. Fatima was a humble but proud woman that never wallowed in pity and this Lillie admired greatly.

After having lunch with Fatima, Lillie slowly walked toward God to grow and exercise a faith in God that Fatima had. She didn't need any more convincing that a life with God was better than a life without God.

One morning, Lillie took a real step. She was seated in her living room at about 5:00am. She wanted to read the story of the man in the belly of the great fish. But she could not remember that book's name.

She closed her Bible and said, "God wherever this book opens is where I will begin my journey. It fell open to the Book of Job. She closed it again. It fell open again to Job.

She told God," I know the story of Job. I have read of the faith he had in you during some of his worst times. I don't think I need to read this again. So I am going to close this Bible again and where it opens this time is where I will begin my journey. JOB!

Lillie Masterson closed her eyes and said, "Ok God, Now What?"

Sherry A. Tillman currently resides in the Washington, DC Metropolitan area. She is employed as a Program Analyst and has been writing for many years in her professional, personal, and volunteer life. Her first published work, "In the Mirror, I Stood" is a story about healing, letting go and living life to the fullest. It is available for purchase online at Barnes and Nobel and Amazon. The sequel to In the Mirror, I Stood is "Ok God, Now What?" will soon be available. She was also a winner of the First Quarter 2013 Spiritual Network Writers Contest; "God Knows the Need" and the First Place Winner of Best of 2013 Spiritual Writers Contest for "Peace Is But A Prayer Away." Comments on "Ok God, Now What" may be submitted to: writeonsherry@gmail.com.

MY SURPRISE

By Debbie Quigley

I was walking down a tree lined path one fine summers day.

Happen to notice amongst some trees hidden and old vacant house.

My curiosity got the best of me.

I walked through the trees to see the old wooden house.

The sun shone brightly on this house of old

The paint had faded from the colour it used to be

I walked slowly cautiously up the weeded stone path

Walked up the stairs holding the banister that once shone

The wooden door creaked as I opened it

Meeting a second oak door carved on it a rose

In the middle of the door a large brass knocker as big as my hand

Upon entry the ceilings high ever so high

I took slow steps looking around

My footsteps echoed back at me

Before me a grand staircase with spindles that looked like they reached to the heavens

The warm feeling I got from this old home.

A large candle chandelier hung from the ceiling

I imagined it on what would it look like stars in the night?

A warm feeling wrapped around me as I made my way to the top

Each step creaking as I stepped foot on the next spot

When I reached the top of the staircase before me a wooden oak door

The glass door knob twinkled

The light shone through the stained glass window out in the hallway

I grasped the handle slowly turning it wondering what was behind the door.

Thinking to myself how wondrous it would be to see and old bed covered in a cozy quilt

Or a lantern to shed light on whatever book was being read by the owner possibly at night from years past

Would my eyes see a fireplace with a large mantle holding imaged treasures from that time?

I creaked open the old oak door the room dusty as the sun shone through the window.

On the floor an old wooden trunk sat on the planked floor.

My curiosity heightened wondering what treasure from the past would my eyes get to see

It took all of my strength to open the wooden trunk lid from years past.

When the lid   finally was open enough to swing it back my eyes were astonished of what I did see!

A beautiful doll looking at me!

Her eyes blue as the skies above she wore a white dress

That was all white lace

Her hair golden in color curls draping over her shoulders and her face

The sun shone on her delicate porcelain face.

What a special day of exploring in this house from the past.

The best part of the day was finding the doll with eyes made of glass.

I knew that years back somebody loved this doll with the golden curls.

I would search for the friend of the doll from the past.

What a surprise !

SIGHT UNSEEN

By Camellia Stadts

There are worlds unseen
The cosmos, the stars,
The galaxies.

Here we have our morning routines,
Our anger, our justified opinions
That overwhelm us.

And at the same time keep us safe
So as not to think about what lies
Beyond our meager lives that we
Have created for safekeeping --

As if we were the ones in charge
Of our own lives and this world
That are truly run by angelic realms

Sight Unseen.

*My name is **Camellia Stadts**. I am 60 years old and have lived in Michigan my whole life, most of the time in and around the Detroit area. I fell in love with both reading and writing poetry after experiencing many of life's earthquakes. It's wonderful to me that I am able to create poetry from the times that life has shaken me up. It has made me a stronger person and I am grateful. Besides writing poetry, I also write essays, knit, crochet and read. I have a son, daughter and grandson, my greatest joys.*

COMING IN TO LAND

By Nicola Wood

Once I was trapped in skin
a clumsy machine.
once I could only be seen
as a glimpse behind the eyes
now death has unfleshed me,
undressed me, released
the essence of me.
I'm a spark once more, luminous
a cobweb pilgrim, going home

The path of return is a rocky road
I shake off dust, the hardness of earth
float in the clear light of the void,
discarding memories, a spirit,
bruised and grey with worldly things
washed clean again. Dreaming
of eternity, infinity and Heaven's breath
like amniotic fluid all around
until they come to wake me.

The universal classroom.

spirit guides review

unfinished business, all those

'have we met befores?'

while I plead karmic meltdown.

'convince me of another birth', I say

'just when you think you're safe, you're out.'

They help me pack my hopeful dreams

unanswered questions, loose connections

So here I am, one more turn

of the wheel, year zero, homing in

fragile, bright enough, a great c.v.

(centuries visited,

too numerous to list them all.)

without identity, unformed, unknown

Is there a bridge between star and earth

a runway, what about air traffic control?

I could burn up on re-entry

I've been writing poetry since I was eight years old. Since then I've read my poetry twenty feet up in the air as part of a creative project and self-published a book of verse inspired by astrology. I enjoy writing about the natural world and themes connected to the spirit or soul which, I believe inspires most of my work.

CANTERBURY-CONUNDRUM

By Betty Whitaker Jackson

I remember the assignment; I remember the day Mr. Sullivan tried to motivate us know-it-all-wise-fool sophomores to write a four-page poem. Yes, it had to be about a trip, true or imaginary. Yes, it had to have a least three characters. And, most daunting of all, yes, it had to have rhyme and rhythm *á la* Chaucer's *Canterbury Tales.*

The poetry part didn't faze me. I have a musical ear and almost automatically fall into iambic pentameter. But the story line—that was a different matter. My world was small, limited. No way could I write about traveling somewhere, meeting interesting, even bawdry characters like the wife of Bath or a lecherous parson. I just didn't know anyone like Chaucer's cast of medieval characters. I'd never taken a trip; I was fiercely protected, sheltered from anyone but positive role models. For heaven's sake, the only folks we knew were stalwart Calvinists. How on earth was I going to do this?

I was the oldest of four (had to excel and be a good example), had crossed eyes and thick glasses, two missing front teeth, and was awkward and skinny, even as a sophomore. I wore plain-Jane homemade dresses and carried brown-bagged lunch, unlike my classmates who exuded style with a capital S, bought hot meals for lunch, and got to sit in the big cafeteria. I felt shunned and often alone and shamed. But. . .

Usually I excelled at writing. A's in journalism. A's in

English. I loved to read (on target to read every book in our school library before graduation). Did I know even then that one day I would teach Language Arts and write books? Hardly. However, this day, I felt as dismayed as my less-verbal classmates, and the specter of defeat rose precisely in the one area where I usually succeeded.

After numerous false starts, I took this problem to my mom, as usual, the solver of all adolescent struggles. I even cried a little in frustration. She knew me all-too-well. Perfectionist. Sensitive, Achievement-oriented. Capable, but with a serious inferiority complex. Life so far had taught me hard lessons. But, she saw infinite possibilities and once more assured me I could do this.

I remember she stopped kneading the bread dough, flour fingered, took my hands in hers, and prayed, "Lord, you know the struggles and the answers. Once more show Betty June that she is as special as You plan for her to be. Lord, You have given her talent with words. Talent in music. Good teachers. Help her with this assignment, and we will give You all the glory as we always do. Thank you for what You are about to do with her, in her, for her, and we will bless Your Holy Name. Amen."

Then we got down to basics, a good old "Why don't you's?" a technique I later used in my forty years of classroom discussions, brainstorming. "Why not make up a story?" she asked, as she peeled potatoes to stretch yet another casserole. "You've read about lots of places and people. You've always got your face in a book."

Usually that was one of her chief gripes. "Why don't you find a friend to spend time with instead of reading all the time?" she'd say, trying unsuccessfully to run my life as moms sometimes do. "Or what about writing about going to Grandma's last summer. Then she suggested, and hit the mark, "What about an animal story like your favorite *Aesop's Fables*?"

Now that had possibilities—or as I later learned the term, that had legs. That was a keeper.

I grabbed my notebook and ran outside to my secluded alone spot (there were few of those, in a house full of young'uns), under the towering pine trees in the side yard. I did a lot of thinking there, listening to the sighing, or is it soughing? of the branches in the wind, and watching the frolicking squirrels, chipmunks, and birds who loved my sanctuary almost as much as I did.

So with a quick, "Lord, help me do this, okay?" auditory petition, I sketched out my story:

Character list:

Sammy Squirrel going to visit his sweetie named Mattie (one of my grandmothers's friends's names), who lived across town. Carried a basket of hickory nuts from the backyard tree, and marigold seeds from the front bed, as gifts, treasures from afar.

Stanley Squirrel, a rival for her affections, but sort of a braggart

Diana, cardinal, every preened feather in place, cunning and fierce--named after my chief rival at school, the rich kid from the other side of town, always in my face about their latest cruise and fancy hotel stay. *Surely she'd ace this assignment,* I thought. (Yes, I was sophomorically a green-eyed monster, lacking in grace, and not quite sanctified yet!)

Harry, the gorgeous red cardinal, strutting and proud— but in real life, star football player, my idol. He even had his own red car. (Closest thing to a leech I knew—went through girlfriends like last-week's news.)

Elsa, a blue jay,(plus her entourage of hangers-on and fawning followers), bold and brassy, always pushing her agenda at the expense of everyone else's. (Lots of real-life examples of this character type in this class!)

Evelyn, my alter-ego. Blue-eyed blonde with a winning smile and the best clothes, straight out of *Seventeen* magazine. She's the beautiful de-clawed cat that sits basking in the sun, swishing her shapely tail, wishing everyone a happy day. She'd never attack a bird or chase a chipmunk; she just IS, seated on a throne, spectacular in her royal-highness role.

Ellen and Dottie, my siblings, transformed in this piece to rollicking chipmunks, always dashing here and there, sometimes endearing, industrious, and charming, but usually disturbers of the peace, in the story and in real life. They'd get into my things. We shared a room. Was nothing sacred? Anyway, true to form, they'd disrupt Harry and Diana's tryst, and foment chaos our knight-hero Harry would joust to make right.

Finally, **Tom Cat**, Evelyn's suitor, who visits from afar, wagging his luxurious tail, preening his whiskers, circling her as if she's the center of his universe, and bringing her a just-captured mouse as evidence of his prowess and provision for her, and his allegiance.

So, I had my cast of characters and began to write:

Prologue

With warming April exuding her springtime charms

The beautiful kingdom of Animaladia lay

Magnet for kisses, romances, inhibitions disarmed

Where wooing, and flirting and frolicking intrigue do play;

And stories of courting, cuckolding's adventures occur.

And chipmunks and squirrels and bright birds play knights' games every day

Pursuing sweet damsels who beguile, hard-to-get, so demure,

And soothsayers, myths' beasts, and king's armies put all in harm's way.

And so began my Animalandia Tale. With little revision, the story told itself, (a writer's dream), and when I finished, I knew it was a winner. Indeed it was. Mr. Sullivan bragged about it to the class, even read it out loud without revealing the author's name.

We were seated alphabetically in that class, actually in most of my classes, now that I think about it. I was always behind Ralph Vogel, a big lout of a guy who, in monotone, read so slowly I thought I'd never get a chance to read aloud with affected inflection before the bell rang. But on this day, in Mr. Sullivan's Advanced English II class, I rejoiced, because I could see the glances of Diana and her cohorts of "the in-group" looking around quizzically, trying to figure out whose writing piece was taking center stage. And for once, it wasn't theirs, certainly not hers.

Meanwhile, Mr. Sullivan, the drama coach, whose teaching I later would emulate, read my poem from start to finish, with enthusiasm, dialect for each character, and rhythmic accuracy as if he were reading Chaucer's words in true poetic form. I was astounded to hear how good my writing sounded, and so was the class.

Mr. Sullivan entered my piece in a national writing contest for high school students. Just as I eagerly anticipated my bid to National Honor Society, and my Quill and Scroll pin inducting me into the journalism honorary organization, I awaited the May 15th announcement of winners of the English Teachers' Exemplary

Writers' prizes. He had given me a copy of his nomination form. Could he be writing about me? "This student excels in translating her vivid imagination into capable wordsmithing, creating characters into 'jump off the pages and into your hearts" personalities, and in her enthusiasm for poignant details, provides dynamic settings, plots, and descriptions far beyond my expectations. Perhaps it is because she is an avid reader and a keen observer, obviously adopting styles of writing as her own. She deserves recognition for her achievements in writing, and I nominate her without reservation." It was signed Francis G. Sullivan.

As I reflect on this victorious moment over fifty years ago, I realize that one's hidden muse emerges, sometimes comes up for air, a time to be appreciated. This piece caused me to dig deep, to recognize characters could be symbolic, that a writer's style could influence mine, that it was actually fun to create something my imagination could embrace, and my writing could accomplish. And I won national recognition, Third Prize. And thanked God.

I went on to teach Language Arts to over 4,800 middle and high schoolers in four states. Perhaps more than any other teacher or professor, more than numerous books about writing, more than memorable seminars on writing I've attended or presented, I celebrate Mr. Sullivan's influence in searching for each child's special voice. It's elusive. Sometimes it's just a couple of words in a jungle of confusion, but when I found it, each time, in BIG letters, I wrote YES! My kids knew that they had attained greatness for that turn of phrase, or for that paragraph, or rarely, for that piece that just "had it!"

And, because one's life-experiences influence who they become, I always had a special place in my heart for the child who exhibited what I felt in that sophomore class. The child who needed encouragement in his/her life, the child whose life was pathetically grey, the child who seemingly had no future. Those were the ones I cherished when the guidance counselor told me, "If anyone can reach this child, you can." These were the foster kids, the ones who had no books at home, the ones who wore the same shoes all year, tattered and mended, the ones whose parents never came to conferences or answered my notes home. These were my target kids. And these are the ones whose hugs I remember when I taught them as freshmen, and again as seniors writing college entrance essays and winning scholarships. There's not another feeling like it!

And for me, the first one to attend college on either side of my family, the one who had eye surgery and finally got her teeth capped after marriage, that one shining moment in Mr. Sullivan's class was pivotal. I call it a Godincidence that he taught me at a time when I was so vulnerable. I call it a Godincidence that I was so ready for that breakthrough. I call it Godincidence that I was blessed to influence other parents' children, and to see the rewards which came from a caring teacher's special touch on a life.

NAMELESS FACE
By Kylie Riordan

Who's the nameless face
that takes but does not give
showing her face
in a sea of messy vulnerability

Without the breath of life
merely existing
seeing only what is there
with intangibility

Timeless face
shines her light through
moonlit skies
and rawness rains

Waves of clarity
birth the first hint of light
And the faceless love remains

Grace wears her dress

with the rising tide

dusting the ocean floor

So it is that the nameless face

without the shadowed mask

has a name after all

Kylie Riordan: Healer, Writer, Mother & a Catalyst for Kindness.

www.twitter.com/mindfulheal

DESTINY

By Kimberly DuBoise

The question of my destiny

burns

collides with the vapors of my dreams

smolders with acrid pungency –

yet I cannot quench the consuming

thought within my restless heart.

Why still unsettled if all is ordained?

Breathing in faith and exhaling peace

I see

the question on my destiny

still before me.

WHAT TIME IS THIS?

By Joanne Mills

what time is this
to hear the thrum
tones through crystal
flesh and bone
this call resounds
each cell a tiny silver
singing bowl shaped
to hold a dove
of love alight
every note a prism
unfolding heaven's sphere

what space is this
tucked within love's
finest gilded line
our path contains light
beyond horizons, past
curves of stars, through doors
where night's veil
was never known, yet we came
to hear our names intoned
to weave a shining cloth
of sound and light
to fletch arrows of desire
washed clear in starlit streams

our boundless flow, eternal
white jewelled branches
where pockets of time nest
glow-globes of space
thoughts whirl an ephemera
of snowstorm-lives, until
we stop
feel this stillness
at the heart
of the beating heart

what life is this
if not to imagine radiance
step into our winged embrace
and speak on one breath
Home

Joanne Mills is a poet, short story writer and author of fantasy novels. She is also a mum, nature lover, spiritual guide and star family contactee, living in the beautiful Perth Hills area of Western Australia with two adorable bunnies and many feathered friends. You can find her author site at https://joannafay.wordpress.com/ and her spiritual site at https://heartstar.org/

THE JOURNEY OF LOVE

By Stephanie Howard

From The First Gasp Of Air Outside The Womb, A Cry Resonates
To The World You Have Arrived.
Your Journey Into Love Begins With Food, Warmth And Care.
And Whether Born Into Poverty Or Riches
Innate Instincts React To Care, Love, Clothe And Feed
A Vulnerable New Born Life.

Like A Seed That Is Cast Into The Unknown, Uncertain,
As We Are Unsure Of What Lies Ahead. So Tread Carefully
Love Is Ongoing And Tests Us In Many Ways
The Challenges And Dilemmas Of Human Joy And Pain Are All
In The Pattern Of Our Daily Space.

Amidst Our Love For Others We Share In The World
There Is Pain In Love, The Bond Of Which
Encourages And Strengthens So We May Unite
When Circumstances Change A Life Journey Ends
Love Teaches Us To Embrace All Life's Moments Happy And
Sad.

Love's Path Is Often Scattered With Ambiguous Signals

Invisible Forces Are At Work, They Play A Harmonious Tune

So Magnetism And Chemistry May Dance With

Timing And Calculation For Romance And Love's Journey To
Flourish.

The Interacting Energies Of Love Are Intricate And Varied,

Science May Possibly Never Explain The Emotion People

Experience And Share With Their Minds And Hearts.

An Invisible Mystery Hiding In The Shadows Of Life.

We Learn In Time To Create Events

And Put Away In Our Minds As Memories.

Love Arrives At Any Given Moment In Our Daily Journey

In A Variety Of Ways.

Unchartered Footprints Lie Ahead And To Go Forward,

Is To Walk Into The Unknown.

Trust And Love Will Ensure You Travel That Path Together

With The Strength And Courage Of Your Love For Each Other.

Time Is Forever, Love Is Forever.

Love Does Not End, Circumstances Change, Events Move On.

A Rose Is Beautiful Yet Has Thorns For Protection.

Love Guides You To Decide Wisely And With Consideration.

To Love With Your Heart, Soul, Body And Mind

Is To Accept Your Life Mate For Better Or Worse.

The Labour Of Love Is In The Pain Of Birth When A Life Is Created

By Two Energies In The Bliss Of Loving, Sensual Moments

Pain Delivers A New Born To Start A Journey Into The Unknown

Therein Lies The Process Of Nurturing Which Begins With Parental Love.

Many Footprints Are Made In A Human Lifetime

And When Our Journey Ends We Can Be Sure That One Footprint

Remains Forever In The Memories Of Our Friends And Family

That Footprint Is Love.

From A Friend, With Unconditional Love. Stephanie Howard.

THE TRUTH OF THESE EYES

By Swami Adi Narayan

Desire nothing from this world.

Do your duty and rest in the Arms of the Lord.
Rest all in the Arms of the Lord.

Leave behind ambitions, name and fame.
This world disappears at the instant the eyes close to sleep.

How powerful are the eyes' lids; are you not as powerful to rid
yourself
of the blinding illusions of so many things that disappear so easily?

Is it not enough proof that the eyes beg to teach us of life each and
every night?
O how you missed the wisdom, o the wisdom of these blessed
eyes.

Only that formless one who takes form yuga after yuga is reality.
Only God is real and worth your eyes setting upon.

Only God is real for the desiring.
All else are false apparitions not worth the setting of your mind
towards.

O how beautifully these eyes night after night, beg of us the truth.

*At the tender age of 21, **Swami Adi Narayan** left home on a journey to answer the call of self-realization. He entered the ashram of Master Bhagavan Sri Sathya Sai Baba, who on their very first meeting, uttered the words, "I have been waiting for you." From that moment onwards, his life was forever altered and placed on a mystical path through their everlasting communion.*

Swami Adi Narayan writes in the tradition of the greatest poet mystics, from Hafiz to Walt Whitman. Swami Ji's poetry can apply to a beloved human, or a divine Beloved accessed through meditation and contemplative practices. Crying out to this unnamed Beloved, Swami Ji accesses the universal voice of humanity and its desperate cries for love. Swami Ji enjoins us on his journey into his interior of most deep and sacred yearnings to become love realized through the longing, the trials and suffering, joys, bliss and ecstasy that only true love can offer, taking one into the heart of the Divine itself.

A TOAST TO AN EMPTY GARAGE

By Caryl Ann Casbon

In Germany, at least once a year

a bomb explodes under the Autobahn,

where the vibration of wheels activate its timing devise,

or near schools, injuring children playing soccer in fields.

A full-time bomb squad still searches for these deadly remnants,

bombs dropped and buried from a war, now 70 years past.

You would think it would be over by now.

Forgotten.

It's not.

It is said that every object has a vibration,

a frequency with an energetic field.

Like the lost bombs of WWII,

my garage stores old family heirlooms: a vanity from Aunt Alice's

bedroom

contains the memory of her miserable marriage to Uncle Dick,

collects dust, incubates their suffering, leaking upward

through the heat vents.

Clutter zones of ancestral histories pile up, underground:

cut glass liquor decanters from my parents alcohol-infused

post-war union—

endless, four-cocktail evenings in front of the T.V. set.

Eight antique glasses from Aunt Betty, now with Spirit,

who generously gifted us, saying:

"Don't ever put these in the dishwasher or lose them.

They are very valuable."

I lift one of the glasses up in the darkness of the garage

in an offering, a sacred toast.

"To Betty: thank you for your generosity."

Silently ask for her forgiveness as I wrap the glasses in newspaper

for Goodwill. "I love your love,

but these glasses have to go.

They are ugly and we don't use them.

They are dragging us down. Amen."

Feng Shui, the 3,000 year-old Taoist art and science

 of the material world, which is the spirit world.

What is without is within.

Keep what is current for you,

which keeps you in the current,

and brings you Light.

Release what is old, pulls you backwards,

is used up, or should be.

Cull your life, and see what freedom

you may find in an empty garage.

Caryl Ann Casbon is a North West writer, speaker, interfaith minister, spiritual director, and author of her first book of poetry, The Everywhere Oracle: A Guided Journey Through Poetry for an Ensouled World, recently recognized as a finalist for the National Excellence Indie Awards. She has worked in higher education, leading the Graduate CORE Program at Lewis & Clark College, and for the last 21 years as a retreat leader through the Center for Courage & Renewal based on the soul work developed by Parker J Palmer. She helped create and lead the International Anamcara Project through the Sacred Art of Living Center. Her other writing projects include: The Geography of Grace, The Soul of Aging, and The User's Guide for A Hidden Wholeness, with Parker Palmer, all writings designed to create safe spaces for deep inner work in community. Caryl lives in Bend, Oregon with her husband and fur-friend cat, Stewart.

PLAYING IT SAFE

By Michelle J. Kaplan

I thought I was playing it safe...

by blending in instead of standing out,

by going with what was known and within reach

instead of risking it all on a belief of something better,

by being self-deprecating instead of stating the obvious,

by shooting for acceptance instead of sharing my greatness,

by concealing my flaws instead of asking for help,

by being practical instead of idealistic,

by feeling alone in a crowd instead of being intimate with one,

by being right instead of forgiving,

by blaming others instead of fixing it,

by appearing perfect instead of vulnerable,

by hiding behind an illusion instead of living in clarity,

by denying instead of giving,

by staying instead of leaving,

by leaving instead of staying.

by buying it for immediate gratification instead of saving to fund my dreams.

by seeking other's approval instead of my own.

by waiting for permission instead of going for it.

by allowing other's opinions to dictate what I do instead of trusting my inner voice.

by pleasing others instead of pleasing myself, when it mattered most.

by keeping quiet to avoid conflict instead of speaking my Truth.

AND...

after doing all this

it didn't keep me safe anyway

because people still judged,

and things didn't go as planned.

There is no safe place to run to in this world.

Which is scary AND liberating

because it finally allows me the freedom

to just be myself.

Which, as it turns out,

is the safest place to be.

FREE – FREE – FREE

By Joan Genske

It is free

Jesus did it

Earned our salvation

He waits for us

It was free

God created the world

Saw it was good

Made one rule

Two People made free

"Don't touch that tree"

Serpent was free range

Changed their minds

Evil became free

"Look! Let's try this!"

Death, sadness,

Chaos, reigned

Choice became free

God versus Satan

God stronger than evil

Choose wisely

Become free

Reject Satan

Choose Our Lord

Happier earth, Happy Heaven

-Thus says the Word

A friendly writer critic of Joan's noticed that she had written the entire Gospel message in one short poem. Joan's one short favorite Bible quote is Philippians 4:4. Read it. Treasure it.

GOD IS LOVE

By Latesha "Moody Poet" Kirkman

The sound of the blue waves rain down upon my soul to quench the spiritual hypocrisies and idiosyncrasies that decline my humanity

I need God to define love and the meaning of everything that is quintessential to my very existence

The orange, red, and blue that sparks the sentimental coast in the hemisphere of my fair intellect suggests spirituality is north of an intimate connection

I am lost

The higher power protests my swollen ego and interferes with all that is not whole and holy

I know God speaks thru the blue waves of relaxation in meditation to define the quiet energy that speaks in stillness.

I listen

It will be through the elements of air, water, and the energy of a fire burning for my true desire to connect with the universe

My soul and spirituality is in the realms of disbelief.

There is a heaven that exists for the wholehearted that possess integrity and grant's the angel spirits the will to live through our hopes and dreams

God loves us for our faith and loyalty and honors our belief with encouragements for greatness

We are influenced to shine like the sun and strive to maintain this wholesome creation of beauty

Although I am flawed beautifully, I am still ugly for God knows ignorance and vanity

The beautiful admiration that holds love's everlasting destiny can also be defined by pain from traumatic memories

The journey to the never ending positive energy that is inside of me makes me cry because I never knew that kind of love could ever exist in a single entity

I have been guided to blind rainbows that make me wish I was never born

I choose to respect the journey because it is necessary although I don't recognize my own growth to evolution

The position that forsakes me from the world and my damaged psyche is the perfect balance of light that appears out of dark shadows to give me the gift of everlasting love

I pray to God this is infinity

*My name is **Latesha Kirkman** and I have loved the art of poetry since I was a little girl. I am very spiritual person so writing for God and myself is fulfilling. I also enjoy spoken word and performance poetry. The Nuyorican Poetry Café is one of my favorite venues. I penned the name Moody Poet because I am a moody person and poetry is the place in my mind that defends any bad mood with grammatical expression. Words are my companion with them I will never be alone.*

POETRY OF EXISTENCE

By Raani

Life is: living, breathing, pulsing poetry in motion

Inspiration, creation, expansion

Life in its highest form

Joy of discovery, joy of life

Feeling myself as part of Creation

Every intricate piece of existence in its place

Breathing together as One

One living breathing organism

God's creation in its perfection

The miracle of Being ... and I am part of it!

A peace settles in me as I realize, through the depth of my being,

That I too, am an intricate piece of creation

No more, no less important, than any other piece

I am a Miracle of Being, a miracle of Life

Unfolding, as God intended

Divine perfection in its manifestation

I have a place in this Universe

Living, breathing, pulsing as One,

Interconnected perfectly

Through every fiber of our Being

A peace settles, a joy in discovering

My part, as One

In the Poetry of Existence

Poetry is something that still just some years ago I could have never imagined writing. I never really read poetry either as I couldn't understand any of it; it did not resonate with me on any level.

As I've delved deeper on my spiritual journey poems suddenly started coming through me. And that's all I can say; they come through me. In a way I feel I have not written any of them as at times they just start pouring out of me. It simply feels like something that wants to be expressed through me. Experiencing myself in this creative process is something that exhilarates and enlivens me all through my being.

My spiritual journey has taken me to depths that are indescribable to me, and as I have let go of those aspects of myself who I thought was me, what has emerged underneath is something so beautiful and precious that it keeps expanding to all aspects of my life; creativity being part of that.

FOR WE ARE MANY

By Rob Stradtner

We gather...

As we have made covenant to do

The Dreamers, the Believers, the Lustful, and the Righteous

Looking neither to the left, nor right, but only to the distant horizon

For we are aware that, standing amidst us, is the very army that was prophesied in sacred scrolls...

(that have long since turned to dust)

A force so powerful...

The sons of man must turn their heads and shield their eyes as we pass

The alarm sounds...

A vibration of palpable urgency

Audible only to this anointed assemblage

Rising and falling in powerful rhythmic undulations

It heightens, in intensity and sovereignty, to a crescendo

so powerful...

The very gates of Heaven itself are flung wide open

And then we charge...

as ONE

Rob Stradtner is a writer currently living in Melbourne, Florida. He also writes under the names: Robbo Stradtner and Robbo Baggins

MY ANGEL

By Cynthia Fellowes

It came out of the blue

and landed by my foot.

A magnificent creature to behold.

What are you?" I asked, taking baby steps toward this apparition.

"An angel," it replied and turned sideways to smile its joy.

Startled, I stepped back, reeling from the unexpected answer, uncertain as to what should be my reply.

"Your angel," it explained.

"Mine?" I asked. "My very own?"

Smiling, I reached out and took its hand, dainty in its repose, soft in its sweetness, light in its touch, unwavering in its presence.

"My very own angel?"

"Yes. I am yours."

In peace, we sat. In the silence, my heart sang.

Cynthia Fellowes lives in New York City where she enjoys acting, writing, intuitive work with animals and studying the Laws of Attraction principles. She believes prayer and meditation help these abilities develop and prosper. She has been a contributor to the Association for Research and Enlightenment of New York's (A.R.E.) newsletter The Open Door (which honors the work of Edgar Cayce, the Sleeping Prophet), sharing her Law of Attraction miracles and interviews with spiritual practitioners. She has been an Animal Communicator since 1997, having completed Advanced Training with Penelope Smith in California. Her website is http://www.cynthiafellowes.com.

EMPRESS OF EMOTION...

By Lydia Fraser

Born of the Ice
Internal inferno
Seed of frozen wisdom,
Germinated by flame

Melting emotions
Flowing forth
My holy well,
I acquiesce

Feminine fluidity
Receptive Ritual
Anointed within,
The Sacred Spring

Ice-Maiden to Queen
Inaugurated by fire
Aqueous Empress,
of emotional desire

THE SWITCH OVER

By Julie McFadden

Funny how God works. Like a swoop of air, sweeping in the room, sometimes briefly, and other times lingering. Lingering long enough to fill our Souls with God-Joy we much needed. Long enough to help us understand we are not lost. Long enough to remind us of the Goodness. Long enough to give us new eyes, new hearts, new minds, but most of all New Life. Long enough for us to know everything's okay.

IN CLOSING

We hope you've enjoyed *The Best of Spiritual Writers Network 2016.* If you were touched by this collection, please do these writers a service by spreading the word to your friends and family, and within your community.

To help support this project, we ask that you please take a moment to leave a review on Amazon. Your time and effort spent crafting a review will support the efforts of the artists within these pages, whose talents deserve to be seen and shared with the world.

For daily inspiration, please visit us at
www.spiritualwritersnetwork.com.

If you're a poet, writer, aspiring author, or just someone with a message to share … we invite you to join us! It's free to register, write, and share on our network. Watch for upcoming writing contests as well!

Perhaps *you* will be the next author chosen for publication!

Other Titles by

SPIRITUAL WRITERS NETWORK

Touched by an Angel: A Collection of Divinely Inspired Storied & Poems

Love & Light: A Collection of Inspirational Stories and Poems

The Best of Spiritual Writers Network 2013: An Eclectic Collection of Short Stories & Poems

The Best of Spiritual Writers Network 2014: An Inspirational Collection of Short Stories and Poems

Reflections of the Soul: A Poetry Anthology

Whispers of the Soul: A Poetry Anthology

Illuminations of the Soul: A Poetry Anthology

Finding Our Wings: A Collection of Angelic Stories & Poems

The Light Within: A Collection of Peace and Prose

www.SpiritualWritersNetwork.com

ABOUT US

We are an independent publisher in business since 2012. At Transcendent Publishing, our mission is to educate our authors on the many options available while offering a variety of services to ensure you make the best decision for your project.

We partner with our authors in the creation process, working closely with you each step of the way to ensure you are pleased with every aspect of production. You'll maintain creative control over the complete process, from cover design to interior style and layout.

With Transcendent Publishing, you'll retain the rights to your work, all while benefiting from the high-quality professional services of a reputable publisher.

SERVICES

- Self-Publishing Packages
- Premium Publishing Packages
- E-Book Publishing
- Professional Cover Design
- One-on-One Coaching
- Professional Editing
- Marketing Materials & Services

www.transcendentpublishing.com